# *the Breach*

## Brian Kaufman

Last Knight Publishing Company
P.O. Box 270006,
Fort Collins, CO 80527

The Breach
A Last Knight Publishing Book / June 2002

ISBN # 0-9720442-0-5

Library of Congress Cataloging in Publishing Number
2002105810

Cover design and illustration: Gregg Kantz
Text layout: Gregg Kantz

First Printing:  June 2002

Printed by
Kendall Printing Company
Greeley, CO   80631
USA

*For my wife, Judith.*

# Introduction

Most of the riddles of history are doomed to remain unsolved.  This is both the fascination and the frustration that history holds for us.  In his excellent work, *A Time to Stand*, Walter Lord quotes an old Texan: "You know, legend is often truer than history, and always more lasting."[1] History undergoes constant revision.  The story of the Alamo is full of unanswered questions that inform both legend and revision.  Did any of the garrison survive the battle?  Did Travis "draw the line" in the dirt with his sword?  Was he killed by enemy fire at the north wall, or did he commit suicide?  Did Bowie die before the battle began?  Did Crockett surrender?

Historians who try to answer these questions must rely heavily on Mexican sources.  The Texan survivors of the battle left an unsatisfactory record of the event.  Susanna Dickinson spent the full ninety minutes of actual fighting in a small room in the chapel.  Her daughter was too

---

1 Lord, Walter. *A Time To Stand* Lincoln: University of Nebraska Press, 1961. 198.

young to remember anything. Joe, a slave belonging to Travis, spent much of the battle in one of the barracks rooms. His account, retold in William F. Gray's From Virginia to Texas, 1835, is compelling but limited.

Many of the Mexican sources are problematic. Some suffer from self-promotion, political subtext, or the desire to say whatever the victorious North Americans wanted to hear. In 1837, General Antonio López de Santa Anna published a pamphlet offering his explanation for the failed Texas campaign. The same year, his secretary, Ramon Caro, published a pamphlet that was bitterly critical of General Santa Anna. General José Urrea devoted much of his report to denouncing General Vicente Filisola, Santa Anna's second-in-command. If nothing else, these documents demonstrate the infighting that helped to sabotage the Mexican effort against the Texans.

The more reliable Mexican sources include José Enrique de la Peña's *With Santa Anna in Texas*, Filisola's *History of the War in Texas*, and the daily journals of Colonel Juan Nepomuceno Almonte and Captain José Juan Sánchez-Navarro. To this list, I add the journal of General Manuel Fernandez Castrillón.

Revisiting the volatile history of the region may be useful in understanding the nature of the conflict. In 1821, Mexico rebelled against Spain, ending colonial rule of that European power. Newly independent Mexico underwent violent political changes, culminating in Santa Anna's rise to power in 1824.

In the 1830s, Santa Anna's turn toward a centralist government angered the Texans, who had an emotional commitment to the republican form of government. Mexicans felt betrayed by a province that had received preferential treatment in tax matters.

For the North Americans, Texas was an open, unsettled land, waiting for an industrious hand to turn the soil. For the Mexicans, Texas was a northern extreme, claimed by the Spaniards, and theirs by right of exploration. (Of course, neither the Texans nor the Mexicans bothered to negotiate with the Native Americans who initially inhabited the territory.)

In 1835, dissatisfaction with the Mexican government of Santa Anna reached the point of armed insurrection with the taking of San Antonio (referred to as "Béjar" in the journal). The surrender of the Mexican garrison there prompted Santa Anna's retaliatory invasion. For the North American-born Texans, it was revolution in the grand tradition of the American Revolution, fifty years earlier. For the Mexicans, it was civil war stirred by foreign agitators.

Santa Anna's army marched north in February, surprised the garrison at the Alamo, lay siege to the place, and after thirteen days, took the converted mission by force, killing the defenders.

One of Santa Anna's most trusted officers was General Castrillón. Born in the early 1780s to a Criollo family in Cuba, he received a fine classical education in Havana. He began his professional military career with the Royal Spanish Colonial Army, switching his allegiance to Mexican revolutionary forces, first with Agustin de Iturbide, the Royalist commander who declared independence from Spain, and then with the forces of the Republic that replaced Iturbide. Changing alliances was hazardous; he spent some time in prison. From 1822 on, he was a friend and confidant of Santa Anna. He spent most of his military career as a staff officer. It is clear from his narrative that he felt slighted by the lack of an independent command and believed his situation would change with the coming of war in Texas. Sadly for Castrillón, he was correct.

The journal begins with the Mexican army's march to Texas and ends with the Battle of San Jacinto. The passage covering the Alamo massacre is richly detailed and offers surprising answers to some of those questions that have fascinated and frustrated historians. Debate over the validity of those answers will continue, no doubt, but Castrillón's diary offers a fresh glimpse from a discriminating eye, and in this respect is an invaluable addition to Alamo literature.

# Translator's Note

A brief explanation of how I acquired the Castrillón manuscript and how it came to its present form is in order.

My ancestors came to America from northern Prussia, in present-day Germany. The original Kaufman was a Prussian officer named Von Heppen, a man overly fond of fermented beverages. Because drinking and fighting between officers was a frequent problem, a general order was issued: any officer caught fighting would be dealt with severely. Within a week, Von Heppen visited a tavern, drank to his usual excess, and beat a fellow officer into agreement at the close of an argument. Realizing his mistake, Von Heppen deserted and headed for the New World, leaving Napoleonic Europe behind.

Von Heppen settled in Virginia and opened a grocery store, becoming Der Kaufman (the "grocer"). He went broke within a year. He moved west and enlisted, serving in the United States Army under Andrew Jackson during the War of 1812. Shortly after the battle of New Orleans, he married Elsa Van Morrison, who bore him a son.

(Family legend has it that these two events occurred in the same week). The boy, Samuel Kaufman, went to Texas and fought in the Battle of San Jacinto, where he encountered General Castrillón for the first and only time.

Years later, one of Samuel Kaufman's sons moved north, away from the Germanic settlements that prospered in Texas after the war. Ryan Kaufman worked a claim during the Colorado silver rush with some success. Subsequent generations of the family stayed on in the Denver area, through the days of the Old West and the labor wars of the early 1900s.

My interest in the Texas Revolution was driven by my family background, reinforced by study at Colorado State University in Fort Collins, Colorado. After the death of my grandfather, I came into the possession of some family documents, including those pertaining to the Texas Revolution. Packed and repacked through the generations without being examined, the documents included a journal written in Spanish. I was stunned to discover that the author was General Castrillón, identified by Peña and others as a central figure in the Alamo drama. I realized that I held the answer to some old mysteries.

Also included in the packet was a letter from Samuel Kaufman, written just after the Battle of San Jacinto. I present it here, at the end of the manuscript, followed by Castrillón's final entry. The sad irony of these two items, the letter and the final entry, will be self-evident.

Castrillón was not always comfortable with a florid style of embellishment that was fashionable in the early nineteenth century. He wrote in a straightforward manner. His prose was direct and sensory-laden. His spelling was inconsistent, not surprising for a professional soldier, so for clarity's sake I have adjusted the spellings to the accepted norm. Otherwise, I've left the journal intact.

I could not have completed this project without a great deal of assistance. Several professors at Colorado State University provided wonderful emotional support, including Dr. Chip Rhodes, Dr. David Lindstrom, Dr. Barbara Lakin, and Dr. Michael McCulloch.

Some research was done at the Daughters of the Republic of Texas library in San Antonio. I owe special thanks to Jeanette Phinney, who made an amateur historian feel very much at home in her library.

Love and thanks to my wife, Judith, who kept our family running while I spent three years "chasing the past."

Finally, thanks and respect to Brigadier General Castrillón. Like the men who defended the Alamo, he responded to danger and an impossible situation with grace and courage. His diary is a reminder of something that is easy to forget: heroes fought on both sides at the

Alamo. When the names of Travis, Bowie, Bonham, and Crockett are remembered, let the name of Castrillón be celebrated as well.

# Chapter

# 1

(*Translator's Note*: The first three pages of Castrillón's diary were smeared and unreadable, so the narrative begins without any introductory passages. The first legible entry describes a grand review of the Mexican army in the town of Saltillo, more than three hundred miles southwest of San Antonio.)

**January 25, 1836. Saltillo.**

You can whip an old dog and it will come creeping back, tail tucked up under its legs, pressing close, never daring to look your way. That is how Cós[1] looked, hunched down, sidling his horse next to His Excellency. The Cós mustache, known throughout the army for its clipped perfection, was in disarray. Sweat pooled at the tips like spittle. His mouth hung open, tongue pushing against his lower lip, while he panted. The soldiers had already begun to pass in grand review, a sudden thunder of marching feet. I could not secure a private audience

---

[1] General Mártin Perfecto de Cós, brother-in-law of Santa Anna.

with His Excellency, General Antonio López de Santa Anna, because his whipped dog Cós would not go away.

Other staff officers buzzed around His Excellency as well, like gnats in an orchard. I nudged my horse, and took a place to the left of His Excellency, just seconds before Caro[2] would have done the same.

Cós stayed to the rear of His Excellency's horse, an appropriate place to heel. He could be seen yapping into the Commander's ear at all times, trying to talk his way into favor, a favor that he had acquired by marriage, and lost by incompetence. I wonder if he cried into his wife's skirts, cursing God and his luck. Why couldn't he have led his troops into another Indian village, burning maize and subjecting women to his little quill-dick, instead of fighting the pirates of Coahuila-Texas? A few more *jacales*[3] put to the torch, a few new recruits in tow, he could have pranced out his days in parade, waving to the women, nodding like a rich uncle to the men, safely away from danger.

---

2Ramon Martinez Caro, secretary to Santa Anna.
3A *jackale* is a small shack or hut.

I should have liked to hear Cós greet his brother-in-law, when he returned from his ignoble surrender.[4] I wonder what pleasantries they exchanged in the presence of staff, waiting for that first moment to be alone, that first moment of broken silence beyond the stone-carved stare of His Excellency's eyes. I should have liked to listen as Cós called on his wife's humiliated name as his only defense, so that every subsequent moment of pomp and pride would be revealed for what it is - a performance, a charade, a cloak to be draped at the foot of the bed when the sun creeps down at night.

Cós must be anxious to return to Texas, though he gave his word that he would not. One need not worry about a promise given to criminals. Honor does not apply to pirates. Still, the spectacle of the brother-in-law of the President of Mexico bargaining for his life with those same criminals should offend everyone who loves the Republic!

Cós must long for a chance at redemption. The force that had assembled before us might offer him an opportunity. The Republic's Tricolor floated past, followed by the rows of infantry carrying muskets. The bands trumpeted as we watched the review. The effect was

---

4 On December 10, 1835, General Cós surrendered the Mexican garrison in San Antonio after a five day siege. His force of 1,400 men had been defeated by 300 rebels. In exchange for safe return to Mexico, Cós signed a covenant, pledging to support the Constitution of 1824, and not to take up arms against the Texans again.

cumulative. As more and more men passed, we began to sense the sheer volume and potency of our force. Men shuffled by in white pants and boots, blue pants and sandals. Dust billowed and coated everything. I could taste the dirt in the air. The music stopped for a moment, but the soft rhythm of marching feet kept the cadence. I stared at the colored pompons that bounced at the top of the *shakos*[5] as they passed, and thought, see how many we are? It was as if the ranks circled back around twice, three times.

I thought then of the hundreds of wagons and ox carts, the oxen, and the eighteen hundred mules it would take to move this army north. We are a poor country, and it will be most difficult to procure the necessary supplies.

Cós nudged his mount forward, wedging himself in to the right of His Excellency. He whispered something in the Commander's ear, and then glanced at me, his face blank as adobe. Caro moved in behind us, his little head cocked, trying to listen in.

Sweat crept down my back, and I shifted in the saddle. I am uncomfortable in full dress - a bicorn hat sits at the top of my head like an egg on a table, ready to roll to either side. If I had been alone with

---

[5]*shako* was a tall black leather hat, ornamented with a brass plate, colored cords and lace. The pompons on top signified the soldier's classification. For example, green for Chasseurs, red for Grenadiers, and tricolor for Fusiliers.

His Excellency, I would have removed it and let my hair spill. My uniform was tailored in Mexico City and fits well, but I am more at ease with a frock and cape. I am not suited to the sort of costume display that pleases Cós, or for that matter, Ramírez y Sesma.[6]

Still, I found the passing of the troops to be an encouraging show of efficacy. The people of Saltillo stood in the billowing dust, hats in hand, heads bared to the sun and the mighty host we have gathered. The rhythm of marching feet was a benediction, and invocation.

I was caught up in a moment of pure love of my country, and I allowed myself a boast. "The campaign will be like this review," I said. "A parade, a stroll that will crush the *norteamericanos*. They will run, or they will be ground under." I could see the corners of His Excellency's mouth tug with a smile, before returning to the salutes of the passing troops.

At length, the cavalry passed before us, pennons at the end of their lances fluttering to the music. Some of the men wore new coatees, bright red trimmed with green collars, a shock of color against the sun-blanched walls of Saltillo. His Excellency was especially attentive to the passing of these favorites. I found my thoughts returning to Ramírez y Sesma, a sour ball of spit in the back of my throat, so I renewed my

---

[6] General Joaquín Ramírez y Sesma, who commanded the vanguard of the Texas invasion.

efforts at conversation. "The army you have assembled will be victorious in short order," I predicted.

"The United States may interfere," the Commander replied. "Perhaps it is inevitable. The *norteamericanos* make good neighbors, as long as we are separated from them by empty territories. As they come into contact with us, conflicts arise. They are too different." He coughed and clutched his stomach.

"Your illness continues?" I asked.

"Yes. The surgeon can do nothing. I can barely stay on my horse." He sat up, as if expending great effort. "No matter," he continued, "I am determined not to delay another day." He turned to face me, his features clouded with sickness. "We must not allow more *norteamericanos* to aid Texas. That is why we must invade in the winter months, when we are not expected. Our swift response will catch these foreigners off their guard."

He turned back to the review, and added, "If the United States sees fit to aid these pirates, I will march the length of their country and plant our flag in the streets of Washington." I smiled, but His Excellency was not joking. Cós gave a solemn nod of agreement, and I had to look away.

"If that came to pass, I would be at your side, my General," Cós promised.

"And I would follow you as well," Caro offered from behind His Excellency's horse.

"Well then, we needn't change position at all," I said. His Excellency swallowed a laugh, and shook his head. After a moment, he leaned over and said something to Cós. The trumpets blasted his words, but the wave of his hand was unmistakable. Cós drew back as if he'd been slapped. He cowered for a moment, and then pulled away, leaving me nearly alone with His Excellency.

Caro lurked behind us. His Excellency spoke in a soft voice, glancing back every few moments. It was clear that he wished to speak in confidence. It was equally clear that he enjoyed Caro's frustration at being excluded.

"Later, when the northern provinces are secure," he said, "our interests will surely collide with those of the United States. Our cultures cannot mix. There will be war. I will lead the armies of the Republic against any aggressor. I have always served my country thus. At other times, it will be necessary to return to the capitol. It is not wise to always be away. Tell me, what do you think of Filisola?"[7]

Filisola. The Italian. In October, His Excellency declared his intention to elevate this foreigner to second-in-command. For his right-

---

[7] Vicente Filisola, Santa Anna's second-in-command.

hand man, he chooses one who is not even Mexican. The blood boils until it jumps in the veins. I thought carefully before speaking. "He is very loyal to you," I said, searching for the appropriate response.

Santa Anna nodded. In profile, His Excellency's face is finely sculpted. When he was younger, he was a dashing hero, cut straight from a Roman mold. He has aged gracefully. It is when he turns his face that one notices the intensity of his eyes, like hot onyx. When he is angry, his eyes burn. When he is happy, they warm and sustain. Today he was ill, and his eyes were coated and shot through with red.

"You are loyal as well, old friend," he told me. "And what do you think of Urrea?"[8]

Urrea is one of His Excellency's most competent officers, but he is also a liberal. I believe that someday, he will present a political challenge to Santa Anna. "A talented man, for certain," I said. "He seems to be a man of great ambition. I am certain he will serve you well if you tether him closely."

The last of the cavalry columns were passing, finally. His Excellency's horse kicked the ground, impatient to be on the move. "Yes, that much is certainly true. Well, Castrillón, thank you for your counsel. I have always valued your opinion." I shrugged. His

---

[8] General José Urrea, commander of the Mexican forces east of Santa Anna.

Excellency had not asked me anything of importance, nor had I responded with anything of merit.

He cleared his throat, and began to speak again. "Today, our country spreads its damaged wings, like an eagle, pecked and bloodied, and takes to the sky, finally able to bring talons to bear on its enemies. The years of rebellion are forgotten. We must march north, to take back what is ours, Texas."

I closed my eyes to the heat that rose out of the dust in waves. His Excellency lifted his voice, and his words took on the sonorous tone of a fine tenor. I prepared myself for a lengthy speech.

"We looked to the United States for a shining example of democracy, and tried to emulate it, naively thinking we could count on the support of our neighbor to the north, although the export of this great social experiment called democracy has resulted in unrelenting misery abroad.[9] Boundaries will never hold the *norteamericanos*. They have invaded our land with their 'peaceful settlers.'"

He stopped speaking and motioned me closer. A single glance from His Excellency sent Caro and his horse scuttling back into the shadow of a veranda behind us. Finally alone, His Excellency cut the meat from

---

[9] Santa Anna is probably referring here to the French Revolution. These sentiments were echoed by the Mexican Secretary of War, Jóse María Tornel y Mendivil, in his published history of the Texas conflict.

the rib. "The Republic has been at war since its birth, and will remain that way," he said. "Rebellion in the provinces, intrigue and avarice from those who proclaim their support, and a nation of barbarians to the north - how could it be otherwise? On those future occasions when our country's interests are best served by my personal direction of events from the capitol, I will need men such as yourself, men of talent, men I can trust, to command the armies. I look forward to the immediate success of the Texas campaign, so that we may embark on the next phase of our country's destiny."

I nodded. His Excellency pivoted in the saddle to face me, his gold epaulets tinkling at the turn. "Does my proposition interest you, Castrillón?"

I measured my answer. "Of course, Your Excellency. I will serve our country in any way you wish."

He turned away. "You hide your enthusiasm well."

I laughed. "Pardon my reticence, Your Excellency. The thought of an independent command intrigues me. I would welcome it." He nodded. I let the subject slip away, to avoid appearing too eager in the matter.

I am most eager, though.

His Excellency has gathered an army, and will march on the pirates that steal Mexican land, and kill Mexican soldiers. We will be victorious, of that there can be no doubt. In doing so, we will take our rightful place among other nations, and the United States will know that Antonio López de Santa Anna will not tolerate the slow creep of the white English settler, or the unofficial interference of a country not yet at war with us.

And yet I must ask - to whom does His Excellency turn at this critical moment in the life of the Republic? Ramírez y Sesma, the timid cavalry mouse, who is already en route to the Rio Bravo[10] with his brigade. And Cós, the disgrace of Béjar, who retains command in ignominy.

I am not naive to the ways of politics. I understand that Urrea is a formidable foe, and must be kept fully in view by sending him off to run certain errands in Texas. I understand that Filisola is a pragmatic choice for the army's second-in-command. He is a foreigner, so no one but His Excellency trusts him. In this way, he will serve His Excellency independently, with no secret intentions.

I understand that I am valuable to His Excellency as an aide-de-camp.

But I also understand that Ramírez y Sesma and Cós are untalented buffoons. There will always be politics, and though the positions of

---

10 The Rio Grande.

these two pretenders seem necessary, I wish that there were enough men of talent, with a proper sense of honor and duty, to fill the positions on the Commander's staff.

I will exact a measure of solace, and no small amount of amusement, when we march. When the favors planned over gambling tables or cockfights pay their dividends, there is still the march. We will press for a month through the desert in winter. There will be no water, and the hardships will be great. When the weather is fair, we will roast, and when the weather turns, we will freeze. Let Santa Anna's pampered chosen try to curry favor from the elements.

## January 29, 1836. Saltillo.

I have decided to continue this journal for the duration of the coming campaign. I have two reasons for doing so.

First, His Excellency recommends it. He said as much at a staff meeting several weeks ago. History will be made, and the events should be recorded. He said, "Each moment from this one will be etched in the annals of time." Heads bobbed like the hind-quarters of cattle moving over rough ground, but I thought, he is right I will keep a journal.

It may well be that of the Commander's staff, I am the most qualified to do so. I have read the surviving works of Livy. I have studied the denunciations of imperial excess in Tacitus. I have enjoyed the scandalous candor of the *Secret History* of Procopius.[11] I know the concerns of historians.

More, I am an observant man, privy to the workings of the army. I am an objective man, having built my career on a foundation of service, not politics. This expertise will aid me as I record the daily events of our march north.

When I was younger, I read poetry, even tried my hand in verse. I am not inept in the world of letters. And what I lack in craft, I can replace with an appeal to the five senses. Let those who read my journal know the touch and taste of war, and how it was to serve Santa Anna.

My second reason for continuing this journal is a personal one. I want a written record of my actions. I feel as if my fate, and the fate of my country, and of our President, are intertwined - at the very moment our country and its leader ascend to greatness, I will achieve the honor that has eluded me. His Excellency has promised that I will soon acquire an independent command. The events to follow will bear my imprint, a solemn responsibility that fills my heart with humility and quiet resolve. In my final years, I will want to relive and savor these weeks to come, relishing the details that a journal could provide.

---

[11] Castrillón is referring to the work of specific Roman historians.

I am mindful of the risks involved in writing down my thoughts. Journals are lost or stolen, and I do not wish to become entertainment, or a political weapon for a rival. I plan to write at night, in order to reduce the hazard.

## January 30, 1836. Saltillo.

Tomorrow, we will march. At last.

The preparations have been poorly made, and it is clear that Filisola, the Italian, must shoulder much of the blame, though even His Excellency has a hand in the confusion.

It has been suggested that our goals might be better served by an attack from the sea, which would cut off aid from the United States in the same motion. Though none would openly say so, there are those who believe that our midwinter march has more to do with restoring the lost honor of Cós, than with proper strategic planning.

Open discussion of such issues is avoided, which makes His Excellency appear unreasonable. Why does he not explain that the Texans guard their coastline with four warships, and we have no navy? Instead, His Excellency responds to questions and criticisms as if he had been personally insulted. We have all learned to keep our silence unless absolutely necessary.

Yesterday was such an occasion. There was no pay for the sutlers, and when some of them approached His Excellency, he exploded in a rage that can only be explained by his continued illness. The staff officers all muzzled their disapproval, risking nothing.

When I heard of the incident, I decided to approach His Excellency myself. I explained that if the mule drivers were not paid, they would leave, taking their animals with them. It made no sense to withhold the money needed to care for the animals. His Excellency listened, and acquiesced, which both encouraged and relieved me. He is, after all, a man of reason.

Some of His Excellency's bad temperament must be due to the tremendous burden he has taken on. He attends to a thousand details, without delegating even the simple tasks. Caro scurries behind him, scribbling notes that he can scarcely act on, given the available time. His Excellency scatters these directives, with no particular order, as they occur to him. (Caro listens, or pretends to. His lips pull back and his nose and forehead wrinkle - a face designed to steal eggs and suck them dry.)

This afternoon, I had occasion to listen to the difficulties of some of our staff officers and officials. Among them was the perfect, Castillo, who has done admirable work securing foodstuffs, pack mules, and even cavalry mounts. Also present were Colonel Don Nicolás de la Portilla, and my old friend Colonel Don José Batres.

Castillo says that the supplies have been expropriated by force, without cash recompense. How will these townspeople survive? When asked for the value of their goods, the commander sends them on a chase, chickens pecking a trail of seeds, going from governor, to the perfect, and finally to the army commissary, where they discover that the commander has not signed the proper orders. In this way they are tricked, and left to scratch the dry ground. There is no honor for Mexico in these deceptions.

I was silent as the others commented on these matters. To merely complain is futile - I prefer action.

More, the discussion became quite political, and I have no patience with politics. I am a soldier. I see things in absolutes. Capture a position, or do not capture it. Defend or withdraw. Fire, or cease fire. The realm of politics is anathema. There are no absolutes in the grey world of government. I shake my head in admiration for the skills of our *Caudillo*.[12]

We stood below the main street, where soldiers marched past, headed north. The weather was a blessing. We did not have to battle the soldier's umbra-mud. As I think of the months I have spent

---

[12] A Caudillo is a Latin American politician/leader with a military following. Castrillón seems to be expressing admiration for Santa Anna's ability to succeed in both the political and military arenas.

marching from one province to another, I can remember every cart wheel I turned by force through rain-soaked roads, as if I were winding the clock of the world.

By contrast, today's march was no different in kind from the review we held a few days ago. We strutted out of town to the accompaniment of music. The people of Saltillo waved farewell. Dogs barked, and old women shed tears. We will look back on this day wistfully, I suppose.

While we watched, some of Cós's men happened by. I could not resist goading them. "Look, Batres!"[13] I said. "These men must be confused - they are used to marching south, are they not?" The others burst into laughter.

We spotted Captain Sánchez Navarro,[14] who was in Béjar, and acted as an aide to Cós. Captain Navarro is a short, stout man with a thick neck that tests the collar of his uniform. He is a strong fellow - it is said that he can win a rope-war[15] with any two men. Colonel Batres shouted out "Are you one of these poor lost fellows?" A look of pain creased his face as he stopped to speak to us.

---

[13] Colonel José Batres, aide-de-camp to Santa Anna.

[14] Captain Jóse Juan Sánchez Navarro assisted General Cós during the surrender at the first Battle of the Alamo, 1835.

[15] Tug-of-war.

"These troops look prepared," I said. "Unscathed, ready for action. Surrender suits them." I pretended not to know that Navarro had been north with the column.

Sánchez Navarro shook his head. "No, my General, they are anxious to revenge themselves against the pirates to the north. They are battle tested."

We interrupted him with our laughter. Batres turned to hide his face. "No, Captain, they surrendered to a rabble without a fight."

"We fought for five days!" Sánchez Navarro scowled, his good nature outdone by his frustration. "We had no food, no clothing! We fired what ammunition we had-" He gestured to the troops marching behind him, and took a deep breath. "You see, the smoke of battle still clings to them!" This last offering was a small joke, as if the cigars wedged in the men's mouths were the smoking barrels of muskets.

"As you wish," I said, still laughing. "We will henceforth consider it a battle, not a retreat that left Mexican soldiers following the ass-end of a compass."

Sánchez Navarro straightened, and wiped the frustration and sweat from his face with the back of his jacket sleeve. "Who can say, my General? I marched with the Morelos Battalion, and I will march again today. We shall see how we fare when we go north." He saluted and turned away.

I was instantly chastised by his dignified manner. He joined the marching column, shoulders squared, the back of his head erect. The laughter must have stung him greatly.

As I write this, I find that I am disgusted with my jest. Sánchez Navarro is a good soldier, and no captain ought to be held accountable for the idiocy of his commanding general. I should have directed my sarcasm at Cós.

# Chapter

# 2

**February 3, 1836**

I find that my thoughts turn to food. We are five days out, and I have not eaten well since I left Saltillo. In fact, I indulged in one last meal before leaving, knowing that the memory alone would have to sustain me on the hard march north. His Excellency has no mess of his own, and I offered the services of my cook, a generosity that our Commander accepted without hesitation. I had no time to locate a replacement, for the march was on us.

The last meal was a huge plate of beans and tortillas, served with a portion of boiled meat. I sat at a small wooden table, warmed by the morning sun. The sky was a soft, cloudless white, like the shell of an egg. The air smelled of damp winter soil, mixed with the smoke of morning fires, but there was a hint of spring in the serenade of the birds. Months too soon, I thought, but a pleasant notion, spring.

The rough-skinned Saltillo woman that served me was a distraction. I would have preferred the quiet to her attentiveness. "It is such a pleasure to serve you, General," she gushed. "I have heard of the grey giant that stands at the side of Santa Anna. I had no idea that you would be so dashing..." I could not bear to look at her - her face was swollen, with a few teeth scattered through her mouth like broken bits of pottery. She was heavy with age, and her bottom was a ball of dough. Even the woman's anxious attention could not disrupt the serenity of the crisp morning. Her comments joined the chirping of the birds, and I nodded, giving no thought to the meaning of her song.

While I ate, her son came thumping through the terrace, crashing into the table, and the morning came apart like a woodpile, tumbling down, spilling away. My drink splashed the boy's trousers, and he stopped, staring at me for a moment. Then he began to cry in raw, heaving gasps that sounded like the work of a dozen saws. The last of the meat and beans lay wasted on the stone floor.

The woman shrieked at the boy, who was no more than five years old. "What are you doing?" she hissed. She took him by the shoulders and shook him, silencing his cries.

"The boy did no harm," I said.

"I must apologize for my son's behavior," she said, still clutching the boy by the shoulders. He stared at the ground with a sullen pout, then tried to twist his way free. The woman gripped him more tightly, and he began to sob again. "He is usually obedient. He causes no trouble."

"I am used to the antics of children," I lied.

She bent down to hug the boy, smothering him from behind with her corpulent arms. "He is strong as well," she continued, "He does not look hardy, but you would be surprised. How is your food?"

"The finest," I said. She beamed, her front tooth jutting out over her lower lip, and it was then that I realized she wished to accompany me on the march to Texas. I decided not to mention the impending march, or make any further discussion that could lead to an offer.

My resolve was to no avail. "Perhaps the General could use the services of someone like myself on the march north," she said, mustering another smile. She moved a step closer, pulling the boy with her.

I turned away, able only to deceive. "I have a cook. He is already on the road, and I will be joining him by the afternoon." The idea of racing across Mexico to catch up with a servant was absurd, but I was stuck with the first poor story that came to my lips.

"I can attend to all of your needs," she promised, as the boy tugged loose, and scampered away. "We would never disturb or upset you."

I shuddered. The old woman's days as a *soldadera*[1] were past. I declined the offer with what grace I could muster.

---

[1] *Soldaderas* were Mexican women who followed the military, serving as personal servants to the soldiers. Soldiers would give their pay (*soldada*) to these women, who would in turn purchase food and supplies. This vocation offered a meager living to most, and upward mobility to some; cohabitation sometimes became marriage.

"I hope we have not offended you," she said, shrinking before my eyes, not in flesh, but in posture, as if her bones were shriveling.

"Of course not," I said, waving her away. My commiseration with her predicament did her no good, and I was anxious to be gone. "I have enjoyed both the food and the company."

As I left, she repeated her offer. I did not explain that the sight of her pained me. I mixed the truth with another small lie - I told her that I am not interested in the services of a *soldadera*, nor do I make use of the favors they offer. That much was still cruel, and as I rode away, she took her humiliation out on the boy, slapping him until he cried.

I chose my path long ago. I am an old soldier, and I have neither the time, nor the inclination to court a wife. I have been in one campaign after another, and the years have kept me in the company of men. That is the price one must pay for a life of service.

On the other hand, I am a man who enjoys the company of a young woman, though it has been some time since I last took advantage of the services of a *soldedara*. There is always a woman for a man who needs one. I consider that aspect of my life to be a burden, much the same as the need to eat, or sleep.

Love is a separate matter. There are times when the price of service seems too high. On those nights, I stand beneath the stars, and I close my eyes, and remember my Isabella.[2]

I grow maudlin. The simple truth is, the rough-skinned woman and her noisy child have no place in my world.

I did not leave the cries of children behind, however, not on this march. Today I saw a young mother shoving her daughter along the road, step by step. The little girl wailed as she stumbled ahead, the mother bellowing over the caterwaul. Another push sent the girl sprawling in the dust. The mother, suddenly remorseful, shed her pack and dabbed at the girl's tears with the hem of her skirt. "I'm hungry," the girl whined. Of course.

The *chusma*[3] follows us, ingesting everything in our path. The wives and the children of the men slow the march, to be sure, but they are extra mouths to feed as well. The marching juggernaut grinds through

---

[2] Unfortunately, there is no information available on Castrillón's personal life, though we can speculate from this and one subsequent reference that he is recalling a past relationship. There is no record of Castrillón ever marrying.

[3] Chusma: "mob." Refers to the women, children, and merchants who accompanied military marches in that era. Though they didn't take part in the actual fighting, the woman provided valuable services, foraging and caring for the men. The march to San Antonio was very hard on these civilians; of the 1,500 women and children who started out, less than 300 arrived. Many died of starvation, thirst, and the cold.

the countryside, like a millstone, and everything from the estates and villages we pass is grist. Our own people curse our progress. The Commander's staff seems unconcerned. The cost of glory cannot be too high if others are obliged to pay it.

We announce ourselves as we advance. Mothers snap and peck, scuttling after the shrill cries of their children. The *soldaderas* chatter with each other, or berate the men. *Curanderos*[4] and speculators try to shout over the rabble. There is plenty of game to be had on the road, and the rivers and arroyos that twist through this countryside are full of fish, but the cacophony that swells from the march drives them away.

The army leaves Saltillo in groups, every two days, as dictated by His Excellency's general orders, so we are spread thin over the road. Owing to the presence of the *chusma*, any sense of order is destroyed. Our supplies are bagged on mules here, and boxed in wagons there, vulnerable to attack, from either Comanches or the elements. The wagon drivers consider themselves ill used, and I am concerned that soldiers will be driving wagons and tending mules before the march is over.

At night, the children, who never lie still, keep me awake, longing for silence. I think of the fat woman with the broken teeth, and I wonder if she realizes the great favor I did her and her son. How will

---

[4] Herbal healers.

the children of the march fare when we pass beyond Monclova?  From there, it is 180 leagues to Béjar, without a city or a town. There is a question that I can barely stand to contemplate - how many little ones will we have to bury before this march is over?

## February 6, 1836.  Monclova.

His Excellency issued orders for the remainder of the march. Included in his decree is the stipulations that all soldiers must go on half-rations, and be paid only a single *real* a day.  Officers must purchase their own supplies from their regular pay - the campaign allowance has been suspended.

This last is considered an outrage.  I would have liked to be standing near Ramírez y Sesma when he learned of the order, if only to hear him pule and cry like a woman.  Several times today, I was taken by the arm, and dragged into the buzz of complaining officers.  "It is an abomination!  It is not to be tolerated!"  It will be tolerated, of course. No one will approach His Excellency to protest.

As for myself, I am not concerned.  I have money, and if I am hungry, I can purchase what I need.  My interests in the campaign assure me of this comfort.[5]

---

[5] This is the first of three references to Castrillón's questionable financial dealings.  He was able to lend his own money to finance the Texas campaign through the firm of Rubio and Errazu, at four percent interest per month.

The men, however, concern me. We are carrying beans, flour, crackers, and other food staples. Why do we restrict our men to eight ounces of hard-tack or toasted corncake? His Excellency has arranged for supplies to be billeted on the Rio Bravo. If there are supplies waiting for us there, why do we starve the men? Eight ounces of corncake will not carry a man and his pack and musket across this barren stretch of desert.

What of the women and children? Filisola, who is from Italy, where armies do not allow families to accompany a march, complained to His Excellency, but was harshly rebuked. Without the *soldaderas*, the men would desert, and so the *soldaderas* must stay. How can a soldier care for those under his wing, with eight ounce rations, and a single *real* a day?

His Excellency was once again in a foul temper. I have tried to stay clear of him. I hope that his illness subsides soon.

## February 9, 1836. Monclova.

A terrible incident occurred yesterday that will make our task more difficult. A wagon driver approached Caro to complain that he could not feed his animals. I watched as Caro sighed, his shoulders slumped,

---

[5](cont.) There was also the matter of a gift from the Cathedral Church of Monterrey, collected by Castrillón for Santa Anna. The money never reached the army of operations treasury, the implication being that Santa Anna kept the donation for himself.

offering the usual explanations, while plucking at his nose with his finger. I stepped into the conversation, interrupting a river of excuses.

"Have you not been paid?" I asked.

Caro snorted, mopping at his head with his sleeve. The damp, chilly morning had given way to a severe sun, and sweat crawled my uniform, making me most uncomfortable.

"No, General," the driver said. He was a thin old man, with wrists that I could have encircled with a thumb and forefinger. I wondered how anyone so fragile looking could command an ox and cart without being crushed, or snapped in two. The man held his hat in front of him, clutching it with spindle fingers that shook as he spoke. "I would not speak for myself, but I fear for my animals. If they perish, what will become of the load I carry? Still, I hesitate to speak."

"Nonsense," I laughed. "What good is a wagon without something to pull it?"

The driver sighed. "His Excellency the President is a busy man."

"I have spoken of this situation to His Excellency myself," I said, "and I assure you that he is anxious to provide for you and your animals. Allow me to present your case." I extended a hand, but the driver ignored it, staring instead over my shoulder. I glanced to the side, and saw Caro's face draw back, his eyes narrowed to dark slits. I assumed correctly that Santa Anna was about to join us.

I turned. His Excellency strode forward, gripping a map that he had covered with notations. I opened my mouth to introduce the driver's dilemma, but His Excellency's sudden rage cut me short.

In that moment, he surprised us all. Caro flinched, and slid away (though still within earshot, lest he miss something), leaving the driver and myself to face the immediate wrath of our President. Santa Anna's fine hair hung in a tangle, and his face flushed dark red. He waved his arms, still clutching the map. "How dare you speak to me on this matter?" he shouted. The driver recoiled and began to tremble. "Do you have any idea of the difficulties I face in assembling and directing this army? How could you know? How dare you question me?"

I would have spoken then, but the tirade was so unprovoked as to leave me wondering at His Excellency's motives. Had this driver already approached the President? Had a messenger arrived with news of a catastrophe? I could not make sense of His Excellency's behavior, so I stood stupid and silent.

"When were you schooled in logistics?" His Excellency demanded. The driver flinched, dropping his crumpled hat. "Tell me when it was that you studied Napoleon and his campaigns? My own officers do not question my judgment!"

His Excellency stopped and extended one hand, fingers splayed, pointing at the driver, but he glanced back at Caro, and I realized that the speech was no longer meant for the little driver. "I have thousands of mouths to feed, and you come to me on behalf of a field animal! When your children and your animals are fed, your worries are over, but I must think of more than just a child here, or a mule there. Yet you see nothing wrong with disturbing me with your problems! What if every man took it upon himself to interrupt his duty to ask for this or that?"

A breeze rustled His Excellency's cape. The driver looked up, as if he thought he was expected to answer the questions. His Excellency shouted into his face, "Would you bleed us dry with your never-ending requests?" The driver tried to shrink back inside his bones.

"I will not tolerate leeches!" His Excellency hissed, and then, almost in the same breath, he turned to me and extended the map. "Castrillón, I have marked the route to the plains above Monterrey. The scouting reports we received were worthless, worthless. Observe the changes, and comment please." His voice had a forced moderation, and he managed a smile.

I was flustered. "Are you all right, General Castrillón?" he asked. I nodded, and took the map. The wagon driver, grateful for the distraction, assumed he had been dismissed, and made his exit.

I pretended to stare at the map. I am sure that my face had drained to the color of chalk. I thought the situation with the drivers was resolved, and I had unknowingly fed one poor fellow to His Excellency.

The Commander's mood swings were unnerving. Was the ill temper an act, born of arrogance? Was he so callously indifferent to the plight of his lesser subjects? Did he not recall our earlier discussion on the matter of pay for the drivers? I handed the map back. "The route seems acceptable," I said.

"Of course," he said, staring past me. "Very well then. Thank you, Castrillón." He shook his head, as if he had just remembered something, and then he turned and walked away, leaving me to consider the meaning of what had occurred. I am certain of this much - our Commander is under furious pressure and needs my full support.

Last night, most of the drivers deserted, in some cases leaving their carts and animals behind. I was present when His Excellency heard the news. For a moment, I feared a reprisal of the previous day's outburst. Instead, His Excellency calmed himself with a touch of opium, and gave a measured response to the crisis. "The soldiers will have to drive the carts, and tend to the animals. Have the officers use their assistants - they can be trusted to safeguard our supplies. The deserters have given up all that they own. We have their carts and wagons, do we not? They make their own suffering."

Today we march again. His Excellency has personally prepared most of the details of the march. He is failing to make proper use of his staff, and in doing so, pushes himself to the point of exhaustion. Also, in trying to do so much, he fails to bring many issues to a conclusion, and details are forgotten.

I find myself wishing that His Excellency would allow his aides-de-camp a chance to bring years of experience to bear on the very real logistic problems that face us. I hesitate to act on these wishes, however. I have spoken to convince His Excellency on a number of concerns, and he frequently offers his consent. I do not wish to find that well suddenly dry.

## February 10, 1836.

I have been afflicted with a certain intestinal disorder that makes it impossible to travel on horseback. I will say no more, as the details are distasteful. I am forced to ride in one of the munitions wagons under General Andrade's[6] command. Every rock and rut seems to toss me, and shake my bowels. My horse is tied to the rear of the wagon, and follows along, riderless.

This incapacitation is a bitter reminder of my age - ten years ago, I would have ignored this, and struggled on without comment. My profession demands mobility. There are officers who command from a distance, but that has never been my method. I deal with my men directly, and I share their risks. My men would never accept me should I become a Ramírez y Sesma or a Cós. They know me too well as a

---

[6] General Juan José Andrade.

soldier. Perhaps I will have to reconsider my station in another five or six years.

One thing is certain - I have done nothing to earn my pay today. I hope this illness will pass quickly. I wish to rejoin His Excellency at the soonest opportunity, and resume my duties.

## February 11, 1836.

We covered nearly thirteen leagues today. This is a miracle, for the problems we have encountered have multiplied. The heat was unbearable, and it has begun to take a toll on the animals. Lack of water has cracked and split the tongues of some mules and horses. This can be treated by stuffing lemon into the animal's mouth, in order to facilitate moistness, but we are not prepared to treat the animals - we have no lemons.

I caught one soldier striking a mule with his bayonet, in order to drive it. The animal's load was clumsily strapped on, and as I approached the soldier, two bags slipped from the animal's back.

I instructed the munitions cart driver to stop along the side of the soldier and mule. "What are you doing?" I demanded from my seat in the wagon. "You are beating this animal."

"Yes, yes sir," he said. He removed his *shako*, revealing a bald, sun-scorched head. Flakes of peeling skin were pasted to the brim.

I pulled myself from the wagon, painfully, and went to the mule. I tried to calm the animal, stroking, and speaking softly, while the soldier repacked the fallen supplies. The mule had been bruised badly, and had several open sores on it's right hindquarter. Flies crawled the animal's wounds, making a nest of the sores. "Why are you beating this animal?"

"Sir, I am not a farmer." The soldier picked up one of the bags, and held it out for me to see. "The beast knows that I do not like it, and it behaves stubbornly to taunt me."

"What methods have you used in handling this animal?" I asked.

"I am from Coahuila. I work in a quarry."

"No, no, how are you handling this animal?"

"With a bayonet, sir." He squinted over my shoulder into the sun, grimacing, his lips drawn back nearly to a smile.

"The bayonet has done you no good. You would do as well to reason with the poor thing "

"Sir, it will not listen!" the soldier insisted. "I am not a mule driver! I do not have experience with such an animal "

"Let me pass on my extensive knowledge to you, based on a lifetime of army service. A dead animal does not follow instructions. A dead animal cannot carry a load." The soldier stared at his feet, rubbing his temple. "What will you do with the goods if the animal dies? Abandon them?"

"I am sorry, General," he shrugged.

I had wasted time trying to reason with the man. "If you mistreat this animal again," I warned, "I will instruct an officer to saddle you with the pack, and beat you if you move too slowly. Do you understand?"

"Yes, General. I am sorry, General." His voice had taken a doleful turn, and I still feared for the animal's well being. "You must be patient. Perhaps we will find a pool, or a river that does not dry up in the winter."

"I am told that the Nueces runs year long," the soldier offered.

"The Nueces is more than a hundred leagues away," I replied. I could think of nothing else to say, so I left the soldier alone with the mule.

## February 12, 1836

Today I watched a conscript die. He was slight of build, and old, perhaps forty years, though it is difficult to tell the age of Indian conscripts. He fell several times, and I wondered if he was feigning illness to avoid the march - it is well known that Indian conscripts are lazy. Mayans, and this old man was Mayan, are stubborn as well.

When he fell the last time, he lay still, pinned to the dirt by his pack, with his legs splayed out. He tried to right himself, like a turtle flipped on its shell. One of the officers put the man in a munitions wagon, but it was already too late. He died within the hour.

Before too long, the wagons will be full of patients. I am worried. There was no physician to attend to the soldier's illness, and no chaplain to look after his spiritual needs. He was buried at the side of the road, noted only by a small wooden cross. It was a sad, bitter scene that I fear will be repeated a hundredfold before we reach Béjar.

My own malady is no better, and I must rely on rest, and on prayer, for a cure. There is no other aid to be had. I am tired of resting in a cart like an old woman.

# Chapter
# 3

February 15, 1836

Night blows down from the north again, and although I am worn hollow with fatigue, I am too unsettled for sleep. Two images come unbidden, disturbing my rest. I will write of the storm, a norther that struck the army yesterday as we marched on the plains above the mountains of Coahuila, and of the things I saw that vex me now.

My illness of several days showed signs of improvement, and I woke in high spirits. I gave consideration to riding ahead and joining His Excellency. I decided to rest one more day, and try to regain some lost strength.

The weather was hot, and by noon, the men were sweat-soaked. Dust coated our faces and worked into our lungs. When the wind started, it seemed a welcome relief.

Then I saw the dark line on the horizon, an indigo slash that marked the advance of the storm front. Most of the men had not been in the northern provinces, and did not know what to expect, nor could they be properly warned simply by saying that a storm was coming. We were not equipped for a harsh winter. The past few months had been mild - the most moderate winter in my memory. The line on the horizon, like the blade of a sword, would change that.

The winds came cutting across the plains, with nothing to stop the accumulating velocity. When the edge of the front crossed us, the temperature dropped thirty degrees in a matter of minutes. The rains followed, driven by the wind, stinging like a straight-razor. The heat of the day had drained us. Now hunger and the elements left us empty and shivering.

To keep moving was a blessing. I did not intend to freeze in the back of the wagon, so I got out and walked along with my horse. By seven o'clock in the evening, the rain had turned into heavy snow.

The column of men directly behind the wagon was led by a sergeant, a veteran, who was distinguishable by his battered face. An indentation on his left temple was covered with a lattice-work of scars, and his left eye was clouded over with rheum. I pointed out a line of trees in the distance, shouting that we could seek shelter there, but his answer was carried away by the storm. All I could hear was, "sir."

As we neared the forest, some of the men stopped to help the women and children, which all but halted the column. I glanced back, and saw the sergeant with a child under each arm, struggling through the mud. I dropped back and took a young boy from him, carrying the little fellow on my back. I went no more than a few steps before I could feel the effects of fatigue and my illness. I concentrated on the sight of my wagon and horse, pacing my steps so that I might not fall too far behind.

There was no protection from the icy gale, except perhaps for the boy on my back, who burrowed into my cloak. His mother splashed through the mud, racing to keep up with me, jabbering her thanks as she walked.

We pushed ahead, traveling a narrow mud path that snaked through the forest. I stared up at the last gray glow of the day, feeble light swallowed by the clouds. The storm shrieked through the trees, bare branches plucking and clutching at each other, like bones in the wind.

Then someone ahead of us gave an order or perhaps a wagon dropped a wheel. The column stopped, waiting on the narrow road. Our wagons and carts would make no more progress through the mud and ice.

After returning the child to his mother, I tended my horse. I blanketed the beast and fed it from the wagon. My fingers were frozen, ice-covered twigs. I shook, my body rebelling against the wind, my blood turning to slush in my veins. In the few minutes I had been standing, snow had covered my shoulders.

Night was a sudden blanket dropped over the column. Some of the men were directed into the thicket to collect firewood, and became lost. Calling out, they followed the voices of others stumbling in the dark, and many went deeper into the storm, their voices fading, rising and falling with the sound of the wind. Some did not return.

I gathered some of the men in a small clearing a few yards from the trail. We piled what wood we could find, much of it green, and I tried to start a fire with smoldering rags and wood chips. Wet snow smothered my first efforts. My hands were fumbling blocks. The men circled around, trying to shield the fire from the wind. Kneeling, still weak from the days spent on my back, I felt faint, and slumped forward. One of the officers grabbed my shoulder, and righted me before I fell face-first. "Are you well, sir?" he asked.

The poor little fire sputtered to life. "I am fine!" I snapped, angry at my weakness. I simply needed a moment to rest. There was no rest for any of us, though, for to lie down, or even sit, was to be covered in wet, heavy snow. Soldiers, merchants, women, and children all crowded in, shoulder-to-shoulder with the officers, sharing the miserable night winds. Rank offered no amenities in the clearing. We shook the snow from each other, trying to pass the endless hours before dawn.[1] It was

---

[1] Both José Enrique de la Peña and Vicente Filisola mention the norther in their journals. Their accounts verify the hardships the soldiers suffered during the storm.

in this pitiful state that I met and spoke with an Indian conscript, a Tlaxcalan from outside of Saltillo.

He told me that he had been recruited by the lasso[2]. The cold was especially cruel to him, as he had not been away from Saltillo his entire life. He stood in his sandals, shifting his weight from foot to foot, shrugging the snow from his shoulders. Ice had collected in the folds of cloth where he had rolled his uniform pant legs up. His thin brown ankles were cased in snow.

From behind us came the wailing of children. We did not turn around to look - there was nothing we could do for ourselves, let alone small children. I offered an angry opinion that the *chusma* had joined the march only to die. The conscript shrugged, and said, "Life is the shadow from a dying fire."

I agreed. "Do you have children of your own?"

"I had a daughter," he answered. "She was a dark, beautiful thing with silk for hair, and black glass for eyes. The plague took her last summer. The whole village celebrated - she was loved by everyone. Such a child dies without sin, and is taken straight to the Kingdom of God."

---

[2] When there were not enough convicts in the jails to suit recruiting needs, the cavalry was known to go into the mountains, and Indian villages, hunting for conscripts. They were captured with lassos and chained together, then marched off for training.

He stomped his feet, while a gust of wind blew snow straight into our faces. "I wrapped her in colored papers," he continued, "and tucked flowers in her hair. The flowers of Saltillo are the most beautiful in the world, did you know that? My wife carried her to the burial ground, cradled in her arms like the Madonna and child. My brother played a fiddle, and a friend of his kept the cadence with a drum. We marched, and sang songs." He shook his head, and gave me a wistful smile. "That is how a poor family celebrates the death of a child. After, we held a fandango. I did not sleep until the sun rose."

I could not hear the cries of the children anymore - the wind was too fierce. In front of us, someone called for more wood, though none of us were inclined to leave the huddle of men. I closed my eyes, and my mind offered a picture of the conscript's daughter, riddled with worms and wrapped in bright papers.

"If Death were here beside me now," the conscript continued, "I would ask him to wrap his cloak around me. I could even take comfort in that warmth."

I shuddered with the cold. "Do not call on Death so carelessly," I advised. "He will come soon enough to all."

"True, true," he said, shuffling his frozen feet. "But there will be no ceremonies for the dead of this march. If they are buried, they will be buried by the snow."

"Dawn will come," I snapped. I had grown tired of our conversation, and I pressed to the side, away from the conscript. Men parted their huddled ranks for me, since I was moving away from the fire. The sullen faces of the soldiers to the rear promised silence, so I stopped, and waited.

Through the long night, we shook, and muttered. The cold seeped through my skin and into my bones, and it hurt to move, yet I had to move, lest I be covered with snow and fall dead from the weight. By morning, it was knee-deep everywhere, with drifts as high as my head.

When the sun finally crawled up over the rim of the sky, we were greeted with a most horrible sight - the second of the two images that cause me such dread.

Snow had covered everything, hiding the true nature of the trees and rocks, leaving hulking imposters coated in white. The sun glistened on the shapes, beams glittering as if on cut glass. I awoke to a world of gems, strewn carelessly over all. Fooled by the beauty, we soon discovered death's touch.

In their haste to gather together for warmth, the men had neglected the mules. Some were left tied, loads still strapped to their backs. The snow had piled on, and some of the mules had pitched forward from the burden. The snow was splattered with blood where the poor brutes had dashed their heads on the rocks. The crimson stains spread out into the snow and ice like red flower petals. Still other mules were covered up past the nostrils in drifts. Numb with cold, heads bowed, they had suffocated.

One horse lay frozen on a patch of frozen ground. It had fallen in the night, feet splayed out to the sides, and split open across the sternum, spilling intestines into the drifts. I had heard of such a thing, but the sight of cold, stiff entrails, embedded in the ice disturbed me. I stared, contemplating the agony of the poor creature, torn open, divided against itself.

Some animals had been cared for. Their loads had been removed, and the beasts survived as we had, shuffling about and waiting for the sun, but the piles of now useless goods were covered over by the storm. Crackers, salt, and flour had been bagged, not boxed, and the heavy snow turned those goods into wet, ruined heaps. We dug out and saved what we could, but for the day our progress was halted.

The storm left us completely disorganized. Lost children paddled through the drifts, crying for their mothers. Merchants dug down in the snow, scooping with hands wrapped in rags, trying to free, or even locate their goods. Soldiers were hopelessly dispersed, separated from their unit, with no idea if the others were to the front or the rear. Officers cursed, and berated the remaining mule and cart drivers, as if they were to blame for the storm. A hundred well-trained enemy soldiers could have rolled the column up like a rug, so vulnerable we had become.

We sent to the rear for more mules. Hopefully, Filisola the Italian can "purchase" some from ranches and villages. I myself could lend no more to the effort. I untied my horse, and set out to catch up with His Excellency.

As I sit now, aching with cold, I think of a baby girl wrapped in colored papers for burial, and of a horse split open and stuck to the ice. My brief illness is gone, but a deeper malady works its damage on my spirit.

## February 16, 1836. Presidio Rio Grande.

As I traveled today, I found boxes, broken and buried carts, dead animals, equipment parts, and wooden crosses, small ones to mark the graves of the children. The march has become a war, and the road from Monclova to Béjar is the battlefield.

The Comanches have caused considerable disruption to our troops. I saw one today. I am certain that he meant for me to see him - that is how these barbarians taunt us. The men are talking about a family that was killed by a Comanche attack, and it is rumored that they commit atrocities on the bodies of those unfortunate soldiers that have fallen due to illness or the elements.

I trust my horse to warn me of any danger. It is well known that Comanches eat horsemeat - for this reason our horses can smell from afar the skin of a Comanche, and react with great apprehension. In this way, I can avoid any ambush that awaits me.

## February 17, 1836. La Peña.

I caught up with His Excellency this afternoon. The division spent the day crossing the Rio Bravo. I arrived in time to hear the conclusion of His Excellency's address to the troops.

He sat atop his fine steed, pacing in front of the men in ranks. His voice was thunder wrapped in velvet. The soldiers stood open-mouthed, mesmerized by the rhythm of his speech. "We presently take up arms and march north to punish foreigners - perfidious colonists that we called brothers. They scorched the pastures that still lie ahead of us and with each step we'll be reminded now - of the punishment that must be meted out to those that would betray Mexico."

He paused, and turned his horse with a touch of the reins. "Death to them all, rebellion defeated! Wretches who murder our comrades, beware! We will not forget the dead of Béjar, Goliad, and Anahuac! Those who dare travel from New Orleans, Washington - are fated souls."

"Now they will reap what they sow," he concluded, "Transgressions are answered in Mexico!"

The speech was greeted and seconded with enthusiastic *vivas*. The march has caused great hardship - I think the men are anxious to take redress against those who have caused this situation in the first place.

Of course, enthusiasm comes easily on a full stomach.

The promised supplies were not billeted here. No one knows why. The officers whisper the most recent rumors, and occasional accusations to each other, but there is no discussion in the proper forum. Alone, these are reasonable men. They are educated, and come from the best families. Together, they are like children. *La política empleza cuando latercera persona entra el cuarto.*[3]

A short distance from the Rio Grande,[4] our men found thousands of jackrabbits, springing through the air like grasshoppers in a field. Killing them required no special effort - one needed only to wade through the brush, clubbing the creatures in mid-air with the butt of a musket. News of the bounty spread quickly, and soldiers rushed into the fields to kill. The screams of jackrabbits punctuated the shouts and laughter of the men. Blood splattered the ground, and the air tasted of metal and salt. I watched the slaughter with His Excellency's speech in my ears. There was a rabbit at every fire this evening. We are ready to meet the pirates of Béjar.

---

[3] "Politics begin when the third person enters the room".

[4] Castrillón is referring to the fort, or presidio, of that name.

Tomorrow, though, we will be hungry again. An army cannot feed on fine speeches, and a full belly at dusk yields to an empty rumble at dawn.

This evening, His Excellency could not sleep.

I do not require a great deal of rest for myself. I am used to long marches, followed by several hours of light sleep. It is not unusual for me to walk the grounds of a night's encampment, thinking of the following day's operations. It was a surprise to find His Excellency sitting outside of his tent. His dark eyes were black sockets in the night, and shadows fell in daggers across his face. "Are you well, Your Excellency?" I asked.

"Yes, yes," he waved. "I am perfectly fit, Castrillón. Why are you awake?"

"I am making rounds," I replied. "Some of the men have not properly cared for the mules and oxen."

"How so?" he asked.

"The oxen must have eight hours in each day to cud, and eight more to rest. That leaves eight hard hours of work. We march them twelve hours, and then tie them off. The grasses here are stiff and thick, and the cattle cannot digest them easily. We may lose many of the oxen."

"Then the men will eat well," His Excellency said.

I stopped, and collected my thoughts. This fine man was the last best hope for my beloved Mexico, and he needed my counsel. I decided that I had not expressed myself properly. "It is not necessary to lose these valuable animals," I explained. "I dare say that not a single wagon driver remains, and the men who are now attending the animals spend their day marching. When we camp, they attend to their officers, who need to eat as well."

"Yes, yes," His Excellency said. He glanced past me, to the north, and sighed. "We must make haste, Castrillón. The *norteamericanos* would reinforce the garrisons at Béjar and Goliad. I am anxious to catch them unaware. I would have us in Béjar in a single week."

I nodded. I felt a certain exasperation that would not be prudent to exhibit, so I attempted to change the subject, as he had. "Will you sleep tonight? You need the rest."

"I cannot afford the luxury of personal needs," he said.

"You are a man, and men need rest," I reasoned.

"The men have expectations of their President. I am at all times aware and considerate of those expectations."

"I wish that all of your staff was equally concerned with the example they set for the men," I said, thinking of His Excellency's brother-in-law.

"It is not enough to match the men, effort-for-effort," he said, ignoring my point. "My efforts must be ceaseless, my bravery must border on the foolhardy, my appetites must be legendary. Every gesture must be monumental, so that I am etched into the men's minds and hearts. Then, when I call upon them to make the sacrifices that war demands, they will do so knowing for whom they fight."

I had a sudden insight into the burden that command had placed on this man. He stood, and began pacing back and forth in front of the embers of his fire. "Mexico does not have an international standing, because we do not have a national image. I am, for benefit or detriment, the only figure that our people may cling to." He turned his hands out, palms up, as would a priest offering Eucharist. "When I make a decision, I cannot simply decide an issue on its merits. I must also imagine, how will history view my decision? I must do this, Castrillón, because I am the very image of the Republic itself."

The gravity of His Excellency's words conspired with the day's events to weigh me down. "Yes, I agree with you," I said. "But will you sleep?"

"I will sleep when the foreigners are put to the lance," he answered.

# Chapter
# 4

**February 18, 1836. No lo Digas.**

We found no water on our march today, and the oxen are dying. Some have *telele*.[1] The disease can be treated by splitting the animal's ear, and bleeding it, but the men do not have the time, or the inclination. Today we ate ox-meat, as His Excellency had foreseen. It was dry, and tough, and sour, and I spit it out rather than swallow it. Many of the men ate their portions - there will be a new, terrible wave of diarrhea tomorrow.

The price of a small meal climbs upward. Many of the officers have newfound anger over the decree that officers must buy their food, as well as food for their own families. The merchants take us for fools, and the men will suffer for it, for what officer would not deny a portion of his men's rations to divert it to his own family?

---

[1] Oxen suffered from two maladies during the Texas campaign. Telele, a sort of heat prostration and Atongue sickness, a cracking of the tongue caused by stiff grass and a lack of water.

My friend José Batres whispered accusations of a most caustic nature to me today - he believes that His Excellency receives a portion of the monies spent on supplies by the officers. Other officers have made similar comments.

I believe that such dissatisfaction is a reflection of the hardships of this march. I expected a difficult campaign. It is, after all, winter. I am dismayed that Sr. Batres has joined a growing group of officers who do not care for, or appreciate, the efforts of the commanding general. His Excellency could do much to diffuse the tensions with a more sympathetic manner, but he is still easily angered, irritated by small matters, and generally of an aloof disposition.

## February 19, 1836. Rio Frio.

Today I watched the sad comedy of our troops preparing a bridge for the division to cross. The bed of the bridge had to be high enough for wagons and carts to cross without exposing bagged supplies to the water. Soldiers carrying arm-loads of dirt and scrap wood to the edge of the river dumped their small offerings and moved on. The lieutenant who supervised the construction stood mopping his forehead with a handkerchief. I approached him. Almonte[2] followed.

The lieutenant saw us, and began to rub harder with the handkerchief. "Your men are hard at work," I observed, "but they make

[2] Colonel Juan Nepomuceno Almonte, head of staff.

poor pack animals. Perhaps their efforts could be aided by the use of the proper tools. Have you no shovels, or wheel barrels?"

"There are no tools at all, General," the lieutenant said. "I have sent for the tools, but did not think it prudent to wait for the arrival of those tools. The column depends on the completion of the bridge. They cannot cross over on my excuses."

Almonte stepped forward. "The river has two sides," he said. "Have your swimmers cross over, and work from the other side as well. You can double your results."

The lieutenant glanced over our shoulders. Behind us, on a rise overlooking the river, was His Excellency's tent. "We have no swimmers."

"No swimmers?" I asked.

"None of the men can swim," he explained patiently, as if I had taken a round in the skull in a previous battle.

Caro, the weasel, came skulking by, wondering aloud why the presidio troops were not available to do the necessary swimming.[3] I told him to wake His Excellency and ask him.

---

[3]One of Santa Anna's decisions was not to make use of the presidio troops, stationed in forts along the path of the march. These men were adept at all manner of desert skills, and knew the land as well. Their absence would hurt Santa Anna at San Jacinto.

"The General picks a vexing moment to exercise his wit," Caro sniffed.

Almonte stood without comment. Caro waited, poking at the dirt with the toe of his boot, hoping that someone would continue the conversation. When he tired of the silence, he gave me a sour look, and scurried away. The lieutenant left as well, having made his point at our expense. The construction went on as before. This bodes poorly for us - there are many rivers to cross, and most will not be so shallow as the Rio Frio.

Almonte stared after the lieutenant, and shook his head. He is a thoughtful man, with strong, square shoulders, and a most pleasant smile. I have enjoyed conversation with him in the past. He is well educated, and knows much of the *norteamericanos*, due to his education in the United States. I have always thought him to be a competent professional.

"What do you think, Castrillón?" he asked.

"Who can say?" I answered. I am reluctant to be so outspoken as Caro, knowing that there are those who cultivate favor with the retelling of criticisms.

"It pains me to side with Caro," Almonte said in a soft voice. "I am forced to doubt my own judgement." I swallowed a laugh. "Still, we may come to regret the absence of the presidio troops," he continued.

"I wonder if our haste to march north will cost us precious time in the end."

I could not disagree. "I have heard that Texas is a garden, where food grows itself, and practically jumps into the harvest bushels. When we take Texas back from the *norteamericanos*, there will be plenty of food for a country so accustomed to a tight belly."

Almonte tilted his head. "Yes, food is plentiful, but we have days to march to reach Béjar, and I am worried about the men and animals now."

"I worry as well." There was nothing more to add, without delving into recriminations. I silently vowed that when I obtain an independent command, I will carefully plan my campaigns, and avoid repeating certain mistakes, as well as avoid squandering the energies of any smart young lieutenant in my command.

## February 20, 1836

The weather was wonderful today, temperature over 70 degrees, and we made eight leagues over arroyos and the Rio Hondo. I ate well this evening. One of the men killed a plump wild turkey, and I had a sumptuous meal of roasted meat and tortillas. After so much stringy boiled meat, the texture of the juicy flesh and the dark, rich flavor was a delight. The tortillas were an earthy counterpoint, wholly satisfying. If God's own mess cook made the perfect meal at the edge of heaven, it would be that modest plate of meat and tortillas. I finished the evening with a sip of brandy. The sky is clear, I will sleep well tonight.

I have enjoyed my time spent alone, writing in this journal. It is useful, I think, to recall the day's events, in order that the mistakes that plague us might be corrected in the future. My entries note the follies and successes of our operation. They also serve to focus my attention on what must be done the following day.

But my entries serve another purpose. I have always sensed a longing, something that my vocation left me no time to pursue. A soldier must follow orders (there is always duty!) and there has been little time for introspection. Now, in these quiet moments, I find that my pen gives voice to this longing, this yearning. Perhaps when I retire, I will give my remaining years to the study of letters. Who can say? I might have been a poet, had my circumstances been different.

## February 21, 1836.

We marched nine leagues today. The roads were clear, and there was good water for the animals that are left, but the men are tired. The division arrived at a suitable camp, a meadow of short grass. Rain began shortly after 5 P.M.

I made rounds in the evening, verifying the efforts made on behalf of the animals. The sun was a memory, a hint of blue at the edge of the eastern sky. Black clouds blocked the moon, and I made my way by moving from fire to fire. The day had worn me, left me drained. The mud sucked at my feet, pulling me down, and the wet, frigid wind dampened my spirit. There was nothing to eat.

As I neared the end of my task, I came upon a disturbance. Two conscripts, drunk on *pulque*, argued and went to blows. Darkness made it difficult to see what was happening. The camp fire sputtered in the rain, throwing shadows. The men watched the fight, rooted like trees, silent. A single shout of encouragement died in the cold air. No one moved to separate the principals. The men simply watched, rigid in the flickering light.

I caught a glimpse of a sergeant, his heavy eyes half-closed, his mouth swollen open. I pushed my way past him, shouting for the combatants to stop, but it was too late. One of the conscripts shoved a knife under the other man's sternum.

At once, everyone was in motion. The wounded man tumbled to the ground and curled up, grasping his knees, the knife blade buried to the handle in his chest. The sergeant, suddenly intent, grabbed the assailant from behind, and other soldiers closed in to help secure the conscript.

After order was restored, I turned my attention to the wounded man. He was a victim of the spotted itch - I could smell the vulture stench crawling out of his pores.[4]  His wound was grievous.  I do not believe he will survive the night.  His attacker will be dealt with severely, and both men will be counted as casualties of the campaign, a loss made more confounding by the knowledge that we have not yet met the enemy.

## February 22, 1836. Medina.

Today we rested.  His Excellency sent Ramírez y Sesma ahead with dragoons to intercept the enemy in Béjar and put an early end to this first stage of the campaign.  I hope he is successful in this effort.  We suspect that our army has been discovered by scouts, but if Ramírez y Sesma can avoid his usual timidness, he can put quick end to the garrison at Béjar.  Our spies tell us that they are less than 150 men.

Either way, we will be in Béjar by noon tomorrow.

---

[4] Castrillón refers to a tropical skin disorder suffered by many soldiers from the southern regions of Mexico.

# Chapter

# 5

**February 23, 1836. Béjar.**

His Excellency's timid mouse has once again failed to act decisively. Ramírez y Sesma's deficiencies may cost us precious days. Our men need the rest, of course, but the situation is maddening. Ramírez y Sesma arrived on the hills of Alazan, a half league from Béjar, at 7 A.M., and there he sat, waiting for an attack from the enemy garrison. The information about the pending action came from a captured spy, who is certainly laughing at the notion of 150 men on foot attacking Ramírez y Sesma's dragoons.

With His Excellency at the vanguard, the division entered Béjar at 3 P.M. and took the cross-shaped town by fire. The bulk of the enemy ran for the walls of the mission, *el Alamo*, while a handful remained behind to provide harassing fire before withdrawing.

When a red flag was posted in the belfry of the church, the enemy fired their largest piece, an eighteen-pounder. This rebellious act was answered by four grenades fired from our howitzer, and the rebels quickly attempted to atone by dispatching two different messengers requesting terms.

The first message came from Ensign Jameson, who acted on behalf of Bowie. The man spoke freely with Almonte while His Excellency received the note. I waited nearby, listening without comment to what was said. Jameson was a tall man in his late twenties, with a full mustache and several week's scruff for a beard. He spoke with easy familiarity, like many of the *norteamericanos* do, as if candor was a substitute for years of friendship. He told Almonte that he was a lawyer - all the more reason to despise him. He claimed that he was instrumental in the fortification of *el Alamo*, and that it was not in good condition, and the men inside were anxious to come to terms. I might have been astounded by this admission had it not been for the state of the man's clothes. His uniform was careworn - the seat of his trousers were cracked to the threads.

His Excellency responded to the offer for terms through Colonel Batres, demanding unconditional surrender. Jameson appeared surprised. Did this criminal expect to be negotiated with, to be treated as a soldier? Vexed by his failure, Jameson forced a grim nod, and returned to Bowie with the response.

Later, Travis sent Captain Martin as his own emissary, asking Almonte to arrange a meeting with Santa Anna. I believe that Martin actually thought Almonte would accompany the President into *el Alamo* to meet Travis! Almonte responded by saying that the Mexican government was not in a position that required negotiation, though Santa Anna would be pleased to listen to any offers. Almonte handled both messengers with pleasant courtesy, garnering information without offering any in return. We have learned much about the rebels - there is a divided command, or perhaps no viable command at all inside *el Alamo*. Fortifications are poor, supplies are short, and the pirates may have no stomach for a fight. I am encouraged that we may make short work of this garrison.

While the messengers were dealt with, the division took up positions around *el Alamo* on three sides, and a small battery was set up for tomorrow's operations. Perhaps nine-pound iron balls crashing into mud bricks will convince the rebels of their precarious situation.

His Excellency was in good spirits today. I believe it did wonders for his disposition to disappoint the rebel couriers.

There was no more fire exchanged this evening. We have been too busy inventorying the belongings of these rebels, and of the citizens of Béjar. The animals were fed and rested (finally!), and the men ate what was available.

*El Alamo* itself is less than imposing. The adobe walls rise out of the grass, more like a pen for farm animals than a fortress. The walls to the south are in disrepair. A large area from the south wall to the church is connected by wooden fencing. I have not been around the entire mission,[1] but I am not impressed by its defensibility. I believe that His Excellency has wisely chosen the first stage of our campaign.

## February 24, 1836. Béjar.

Early this morning, we erected another battery on the river, some 350 yards from *el Alamo*, consisting of a mortar and two nine-pounders. We fired at the west wall with great accuracy, dismounting both cannon on that wall, including the eighteen-pounder.[2]

Men from the San Luis Battalion moved into the houses in *La Villita*.[3] The enemy fired from ditches outside of *el Alamo*, and several of our men were killed or wounded.

His Excellency risked his life needlessly, riding within rifle range of the fort. The men were cheered by his bravery, and I find that I am

---

[1] The Alamo was not a fortress, but a Spanish mission built in the early 1700s, in order to facilitate settlers and bring Christianity to the Coahuiltecan Indians. The chapel that everyone associates with the Alamo was begun in 1757, after the collapse of a previous structure.

[2] Castrillón refers to specific cannon by the size of the roundshot the piece could fire. The eighteen-pounder could fire an eighteen-pound solid iron ball. (The tube from that particular piece is on display in the Alamo courtyard today.)

[3] A cluster of small houses and shacks, originally used to house the wives and lovers of the Spanish soldiers garrisoned there. At the time of the assault, *La Villita* was regarded as a disreputable part of San Antonio.

happy to see him take charge of events in such a forceful manner. His disposition again seemed improved, despite the failure of today's attack.

This afternoon I went with the men from the Matamoros to gather timber from the houses of Béjar, and of *La Villita*, for use in constructing a bridge across the river. His Excellency is anxious to guarantee the surrender of the rebels. A bridge will be needed to expedite reinforcements, and bring across the twelve-pounders, should they still be necessary. When we entered one of the shacks, I was greeted by a handsome woman in her mid-thirties, who seemed dismayed to see us. When I assured her that her safety was my concern, she brought her daughter into view.

Perhaps I have lived too long among soldiers, but it seemed to me that when I saw the girl, the world paused for a moment, and I could not speak, or breathe, or even think. It is said that the women of the northern provinces are more beautiful than those of the southern. Though I cannot speak for the rest, this one young girl could have proven the point to all who would contest it. Her hair was dark, lush, and full, the tresses of an angel. She had the dark brown eyes of a deer. She blinked once, and then smiled. I was captured.

I bowed, and introduced myself. "I am General Manuel Fernandez Castrillón, acting under direct orders from His Excellency, General Antonio López de Santa Anna. Please consider me at your service."

The girl's mother offered her hand, and I brushed it with my lips, glancing at the daughter as I did so. The mother smiled knowingly.

"Are you alone?" I asked. "Are you not worried for the safety of yourself and your daughter?"

She laughed. "We have the protection of the great Mexican army. Why then should we worry?"

I struggled to regain my composure. My eyes returned once again to the girl, poorly dressed, in little more than rags. I was conscious of her body - the castoffs did little to preserve her virtue, but rather, allowed her natural shape to lunge and stab the eyes. All the while, she wore the faint smile of a child. For a brief moment, she reminded me of someone.

"Your situation is precarious," I admonished. "The rebels are a stubborn lot, and your small house is within range of their rifles and cannon."

Soldiers had entered the house, and begun removing the useful wood from the structure. The mother watched the demolition, and then turned back, smiling. "Are you here to save us from rebel gunfire, or take wood?"

"Both, I confess." I am certain that I blushed. The girl smiled. I could not tell if she liked me, or was laughing at me.

"Your confession is unnecessary," the mother sighed. "I can see what you want here."

In a difficult situation, a gentleman can always rely on proper manners. I made a few more moments of small talk, and then excused myself, repeating my offer of service, should any crisis arise that my aid could resolve. I bowed, the girl smiled again, and I was gone.

The air was still and dry outside. I took a huge breath, seeking relief from an almost overwhelming urge, an urge that had not visited me with such intensity in years.

Our bands played music throughout the night, in order to unnerve the rebels. The happy rhythms echoed my mood, and the audacious brass notes put a certain strut in my step as I made my rounds. One sentry, startled by my brisk approach, nearly dropped his musket. He was a stripling, a slight fellow who stood barely as tall as my chest. When I saw how he shook, I allowed him a smile of reassurance.

It amuses me to inspect the camps full of tired young men wrapped in blankets. I will be awake before any of them, tending my duties when the sun comes up. I am an older man, but I am fit, the match of any younger man in the camp.

I believe that I will return to see the woman and her daughter tomorrow. They may yet need the assistance of a gentleman.

## February 25, 1836. Béjar.

It is late. I am tired. The night wind invades the house I use as quarters, whistling through the cracks and windows, blowing dust everywhere. A moment ago, I went to the window, and saw the flicker of fire in *La Villita*. The enemy is burning houses that are close to the fort. Despite the outcome of today's action, they recognize the danger in allowing a secured approach to their position.

Today we erected two more batteries, one to the south, and one to the southeast, in view of the mission church. These two batteries are linked by the Matamoros battalion, entrenched between the two positions. Cavalry is posted in the hills to the east.

Early this morning, we sent 200 men creeping through the *jacales*[4] of *La Villita*. Emerging from cover a few dozen yards from the southwest corner of the mission, they rushed forward across the open ground. It was hoped that they could take the south gate, and make quick work of this siege. The rebels opened fire, with muskets, rifle, and cannon, and our men were stopped with grievous loss.

Viewing the battle from the south, I suggested to His Excellency that if he wished to save any of the men's lives, he should withdraw them immediately. He glanced to the side, his face twisted in a scowl. The other officers stood silent. I held His Excellency's gaze, waiting for

---

[4] Shacks or small huts.

a response, and I had the sudden impression that I had replaced poor planning and shoddy execution as His Excellency's primary source of irritation. Then he sighed, and issued the order to retire, much to my relief.

Later, His Excellency sent Colonel Bringas south with a strong message to General Gaona, demanding that he rush the Almada, the Toluca, and Zappadores to Béjar. It was clear that the failure to take the south gate was a great frustration to him. I had expected the rebels to surrender by now, and I believe that His Excellency expected the same.

As he spoke, the rebels fired their eighteen-pounder, and I stepped aside to watch. I thought of the girl and her mother, and worried for their safety. Their house was within easy distance of the rebel guns. At length, His Excellency noticed that I was preoccupied. "You are not giving me your full attention, Castrillón," he complained.

My lack of manners confounded me. "I am sorry, Your Excellency," I said. "It has been an eventful day."

"You have been through too many battles to be startled by the sound of cannon," he said, his voice careful and moderate as is my own. This is a trick His Excellency uses when he is at his best - he elicits a sense of camaraderie with his staff simply by the rhythm and tone of his speech. I am aware that he does this. I respond none-the-less.

"I am concerned for someone," I explained. "When I was searching the houses for timber yesterday, I came across a woman and her daughter. The daughter was little more than a girl, though she was refined and appeared to be educated. She was quite beautiful, Your Excellency, and she affected me very deeply."

He tilted his head and stared. "Castrillón, this is quite unlike you." He began to walk around me in a circle, nodding to himself. "This young girl must have been unusual indeed for you to take note in this way."

I sighed. "Yes, Excellency. She was exquisite." As I spoke, a strong gust of wind whipped past, chilling us.

He smiled. "I should like to meet this girl of yours. Arrange it."

I did not believe my ears. "I am sorry, Your Excellency. What is it that you want me to do?"

"I want to meet this girl. Go arrange it with her mother."

I stared at this man, on whom I had pinned my hopes for advancement, and hopes for the greatness of our nation. I saw a middle-aged man with dark circles cut under his red eyes. The wind whipped his cape around his gaunt frame. I thought of the young girl, and shook my head.

"Your Excellency -" I hesitated. There were men standing near, and I was reluctant to share the conversation. "I would follow any legitimate order you would care to issue, but this is not a military matter. I beg you to find someone else to carry out this request."

His eyes turned black as I watched him. "Very well," he whispered. "Good evening, Castrillón." At that moment, Almonte arrived with others. I wrestled with two impulses - the desire to explain my reluctance and defer any anger His Excellency had as a result of my refusal, and the desire to remove myself from the scene of this most insulting request. In the end, I made good an exit.

Early this evening, I returned to the shack where I had first encountered the woman and her daughter. It was my intention to warn her against any proposition from His Excellency. It was a course of action that I did not take without reservation. I risk my position by opposing His Excellency's whim. In the end, it did not matter. Santa Anna had sent Colonel Miñon[5] as an emissary, and the woman was involved in negotiations when I arrived.

The young girl sat to the side, delicate hands folded in her lap, unaware of the blight that threatened her. The girl's mother was insistent in the demand that His Excellency marry the girl. "Santa Anna may be your Commander," she proclaimed, "but he does not command me. You may tell your Santa Anna that if he wishes for the company of my daughter, he will do so with proper respect for my family." Her

---

[5] Colonel José Vicente Miñon, staff officer to Santa Anna.

head thrown back, eyes flashing defiance, she was not to be dissuaded. I believe that I saw a hint of a smile on the young girl's face as she watched her mother. I left without any further involvement, knowing that Santa Anna would not be able to meet the woman's demands. He is already married.

## February 26, 1836. Béjar.

Another north wind blew through town today, recalling the one that killed fifty oxen on the march from Saltillo. The temperature dropped below forty degrees. It was warmer later in the day, but the wind kept on, driving dust through the tall grass.

The enemy has stopped returning our cannon fire, except for an occasional round. They sent a group of men outside the walls for water and supplies, but our *cazadores*[6] turned them back in short order. I suspect that their situation is becoming more desperate each hour. I am once again confident that their surrender is close at hand. I, for one, will be relieved. We have wasted too many men already on this rabble. It is a tragedy to shed Mexican blood for such an insignificant fort.

The troops have kept a steady pace of bugle calls through the evening and night, to disrupt the sleep of the enemy. Some of the rebels had no intention of sleeping. A raiding party burned still more houses

---

[6] *Cazadores* were Mexican light infantrymen, equipped with .61-caliber British Baker rifles.

in *La Villita*. When morning comes, I believe that we will find there are no more houses standing between the trenches of the San Luis Potosi battalion and the walls of *el Alamo*. It is unfortunate. The *jacales* made excellent cover.

This evening, His Excellency was "married" to the young girl I met two days ago. The mother insisted on the ceremony, and one of the officers posed as clergy in order to carry out the farce. As I write, Santa Anna is taking the girl's virtue from her.

I can hardly bear the thought of that young girl, squandered on a man who believes that the world is his orchard, and that he may pluck any apple, take a bite, and throw the rest to the ground, food for the insects.

When I consider what His Excellency offers her, I reason that even I might have been a more satisfactory choice for the girl. I could have made her laugh. I know how to listen when a young tongue darts over light thoughts. I remember I felt the same once, forty battles ago.

The girl will provide him a diversion for a while. Then he will send her back to Mexico City, and she will discover what every soldier and officer here knows - that she has been shamed and degraded, and has squandered her virtue for nothing.

This was a bitter lost chance. I have misfired, I am overrun with weeds -

## February 27, 1836. Béjar.

The wind still blows down from the north. At night, the men shiver themselves to sleep, curled on the ground. The enemy does not sleep. We can hear them digging and hammering inside the walls of *el Alamo*. We can hear their muffled curses. I wonder what surprises they have in store for us - they have had five days to prepare for an assault.

His Excellency has made statements that cause me great unrest. Today he told an aid that he should be pistol-whipped if he fails to execute every one of the enemy in *el Alamo*. He is having trouble sleeping again, and he is acting on emotion, rather than following the finer thought processes. There are certain expectations one must have of war, and the custom of taking prisoners is beyond dispute, red flag in the church tower or no.

The sky tonight is blacker than ink. I can smell the smoke of a thousand camp fires. They struggle in the night like candles in a church, flickering pecks of fire, grappling with the elements.

The wind has made me melancholy. I was thinking of Isabella tonight, and how my life might have been altered if she had lived. We would have married, and lived on her father's estate. Or perhaps not. I have been a soldier for so long that I cannot imagine any other life. Poor Isabella. She would have waited at home, watching the seasons pass, growing old while I made my career.

I do not believe I will be granted an independent command after this campaign has ended. His Excellency and I do not share the same vision. There are too many generals in this army, and many of them will be glad to agree with whatever he says, bobbing their heads, swallowing what he offers, without regard to what is right, and what is proper.

## February 28, 1836. Béjar.

The Sabbath has been rainy, and cold. Rumors are multiplying about possible aid to the garrison in *el Alamo*. We know that Fannin[7] is bringing five hundred men from Goliad, and Houston[8] is bringing seven hundred more. This news distressed His Excellency at the staff meeting this morning. He is angry that we have not yet taken *el Alamo*, despite six days of bombardment. The rebels are stubborn, and the walls resist our guns. We will not take down those thirty-inch walls with nine-pound cannon at three hundred yards.

I watched Almonte as the meeting progressed. He stared at the floor in front of him without comment, other than to nod whenever His Excellency directed a comment his way. His silence troubles me.

The news of Fannin's march was particularly distressing to His Excellency. "It may turn out to be an element in our favor," I offered.

---

[7] James Fannin, commander of a Texan force of 350 men in Goliad.
[8] Sam Houston, commander-in-chief of the Texan army.

"*El Alamo* can be taken by our troops at will. What matter to us if the enemy loses a hundred and fifty men, or seven hundred men? That place is not defensible. Let them come, and join the other rats in the rain barrel."

His Excellency jerked in his seat, his head snapping to the side. He pounded the table. We were silent, and I think Almonte shut his eyes. Then His Excellency excused himself, and swallowed a small dose of opium, in order to collect his thoughts.

"Castrillón," he said at length, "it would not do for the men in the trenches to wonder from what direction Fannin's army, or Houston's army for that matter, will try to fight their way in. Our containment would be risked, as well as the lives of men who would fight on two fronts simultaneously. I will not, I repeat, will not allow these foreign pirates to escape. We will have our Battle of Medina[9], and this campaign will be over."

We demurred, of course. It was a pointless discussion to begin with. I have chronicled the events merely to give a taste of His Excellency's

---

[9] As a young lieutenant, Santa Anna fought with General Joachín de Arrendondo at the Medina River in 1813 against "The Republican Army of the North." The rebels were beaten and destroyed. Arredondo offered no quarter, and less than 100 of the 850 Americans involved survived. Many of those killed were hung from trees as a reminder to other would-be revolutionaries. Santa Anna was decorated for his efforts, having formulated his ideas on the proper way to crush a rebellion.

unbending demeanor. Our staff meetings do not consist of the exchange of ideas, but rather, the handing down of His Excellency's edicts. He asks no one's counsel, and he offers no clue of his thoughts save their fruit; his orders, fully realized.

## February 29, 1836. Béjar.

Ramírez y Sesma is, at this moment, marching east to intercept Fannin,[10] with the Allende battalion and the Delores cavalry regiment. I have been given the task of maintaining our containment by stretching the Matamoros and Jimenez. We are spread thin by these changes.

Private Alvarez of the San Luis was sent too close to the south wall on some errand. It was thought that he was out of range. He was not. These *norteamericanos* are able to shoot their rifles with accuracy to nearly three hundred yards, three times the distance our English muskets can fire. Even our *cazadores* can not match the skill of these pirates. Rebel marksmanship is one more aspect of the protracted siege that has caused our army grief.

Today saw the most intense shelling of the siege. We fired hundreds of rounds into *el Alamo*. Aside from their rifles, the rebels are not answering back. They did not fire more than three or four cannon

---

[10] Fannin was not marching anywhere. He was still in Goliad, having elected not to come to the aid of the Alamo garrison.

rounds the entire day. Could their powder reserves be already depleted? Were they so poorly prepared for battle?

I will be on watch the better part of the night. The wind has shifted, and it is not as cold as the past few days, a small blessing.

# Chapter

# 6

**March 1, 1836.  Béjar.**

The wind stopped, finally, but the cold was unrelenting.  At three a.m., during my watch, a small group of reinforcements arrived and entered *el Alamo*.  The night sky was a black cloak, so dark that the rebel sentries did not recognize their own, and fired on them.  There could not have been many, perhaps two dozen.[1]

I slept poorly in my quarters in Béjar.  Later, I had an unpleasant encounter with His Excellency, who rode out to inspect the mill battery site.  As with our other sites, Santa Anna feels he must personally review the location before issuing the orders.  Aside from our initial efforts, when we disarmed the rebel's eighteen-pounder, our west and southwest emplacements have been ineffective.  The mill location is 800 yards

---

[1] Castrillón is referring to thirty-two men from the nearby town of Gonzales, who passed through the thin east lines of the Mexican army and entered the Alamo through the south gate.  Legend has it that the men inside the mission fired on the reinforcements, wounding one man in the foot.

north of the Alamo and does not appear to be any more promising than the others, although a site to the southeast of the Alamo may yield better results. We have not breached the walls, and we have not effected a surrender. His Excellency viewed the site from horseback, and did not speak to me at first. In the distance, the north wall of the mission looked like a thin white rail, crouched down in the scrub. Rather than prolong the coming rebuke, I approached him on foot and greeted him.

"The foreigners received reinforcements last night," he said.

I nodded. "Two dozen, perhaps -"

"Ramírez y Sesma has determined that the garrison at Goliad will not be coming." He sighed. "That, at least, will spare me the spectacle of several hundred pirates quietly winding their way through our lines."

There was no proper answer, and so I was silent.

"I have ordered Ampudia[2] to dig more gun emplacements. The enemy will not be able to judge the location of our final assault by the location of our emplacements, as we will have emplacements on all four sides."

"Have you determined that a final assault is necessary?" I asked. "The rebels may surrender."

"I am weary of waiting for their surrender!" His Excellency snapped. He paused and took a deep breath. "There will be no prisoners in battle

---

[2] Lt. Colonel Pedro Ampudia, Santa Anna's artillery commander.

that comes, and the Texans will understand what happens to those who oppose the Republic!" His eyes had become a whirl of black steel, and his horse, sensing the President's emotion, sidestepped nervously. I bowed, and turned to go.

"Castrillón," he called. "I do not want any more reinforcements through our lines."

Nor do I, though the task of keeping them out becomes more difficult when prime troops are sent with Ramírez y Sesma to chase geese in the east. Over the past few days, tiny groups of reinforcements have arrived here from neighboring settlements, only to be turned away by our troops. This one poor column, two dozen men, will not alter our fortunes.

This afternoon, the rebels fired on the town of Béjar, and put a twelve-pound ball into the Yturri house.[3] His Excellency was still reconnoitering battery positions, and was unharmed. I was worried for His Excellency's new "bride," but Almonte assured me that she was unharmed as well.

## March 2, 1836. Béjar.

Cós arrived today, ahead of his troops. By tomorrow, Gaona[4] will be here. Filisola will be here with the twelve-pounders by the seventh.

---

[3] Santa Anna's headquarters in San Antonio.

[4] General Antonio Gaona.

If these stubborn rebels intend to hold out until the bitter end, so be it. With the larger guns, we can take down the walls of *el Alamo* in just a few hours.

The bombardment continues. The enemy returns fire a few times a day, mostly without effect, and since we have learned to keep the proper distance, even their rifles have ceased to take a toll.

The enemy does not have the manpower to tend all of their cannon. *El Alamo* has eighteen cannon, and even using half-crews, it would take the entire garrison to man that many pieces.[5] The rebel's eighteen-pounder requires a fifteen man crew to take full advantage of the capabilities of the piece. These pirates are well armed, but many pieces will fire only once, should we take the fort by assault. They cannot man both the cannon and the walls. Surely they are aware of this!

The enemy has made numerous sallies to collect wood from *La Villita*. It is clear that they were not prepared for an extended siege. If they do not have firewood, can they have sufficient food stores? I think not.

---

[5] A gun crew consists of a spongeman, who swabs the tube to put out live embers; ammunition handlers; a loader, who inserts the gunpowder charge; a ventman, who supervises the firing vent; a gunner, who adjusts the elevation and deflection with the use of gun screws; and additional crew to move the gun and haul supplies. (Albert A. Nofi, *The Alamo and the Texas War for Independence* Conshohoken, PA: Combined Books, 1992).

His Excellency is impatient. I hope that he can summon the necessary wisdom to avoid a costly frontal assault. The rebel garrison cannot last much longer.

## March 3, 1836. Béjar.

At last, a moment of joy and celebration. We received dispatches from General Urrea. He routed the rebels at San Patricio four days ago, killing and capturing half of them. The bells of the San Fernando Church were rung, and *vivas* were shouted as a second red flag was raised. At the same time, the Aldama, the Toluca, and the Zapadores arrived in full dress, and in full sight of the enemy. It can not be a happy time for these pirates, who by now must realize their fate.[6]

I toasted our victory with Batres. We sat in my room, where the sunlight poured through the open window onto my small table and lit the mescal bottle. The liquor was fire, and we laughed until our stomachs ached. Surely the foreigners see the folly of continued resistance. Surrender must be hours away. Almonte stopped in to say hello. He told me that he sees the end of the campaign in sight, and that he will be home in a few months.

---

[6] There is good evidence that the Texans misinterpreted the sounds of celebration; they saw the arrival of reinforcements, and assumed that the revelry marked the first appearance of Santa Anna. Travis said as much in a letter written March 3rd. They had no way of knowing that Santa Anna had been in San Antonio since the start of the siege.

Home. I am sick of military life, and I will retire when we return to Mexico. I am no longer comfortable in my role as aide-de-camp to Santa Anna. Batres is aware that I am discontented. "You are too bold with the President," he told me. "Do you see the rest of the staff challenging him as you are so fond of doing?"

"I do not challenge him for sport," I said. I poured Sr. Batres another glass of mescal, and then filled my own glass. The bottle was draining, but my thoughts were ordered. "There is not a man in the army who could not offer suggestions for improvement on the performance of the officers in charge."

Batres laughed and poked me in the chest with his finger. "Listen to yourself, my friend. You argue for the thoughts of the soldiers who were captured in villages, or taken from prisons. You speak like the *norteamericanos*."

"There is no reason to insult me, Batres," I said. "Still, if a convict can offer sage advice, should we not listen? And what does that say of those who ought to heed that advice? We have lost so many men! The march gutted our ranks. And the women and children! How many perished in the snow? For what? So we could sit for ten days watching the pirates fortify their position? So they could pick away at our ranks with their long rifles?"

"Bah," he spat. "The rebels. I am sick of thinking about them. These pirates have no skills. There are a few hunters who treat us like squirrels in a tree. When we assault these rebels, they will break and beg for mercy. And there will be none."

I nodded, suddenly hushed. "What you say may well be true. His Excellency has been most emphatic on the matter of prisoners. What have you to say to that?"

He answered slowly, tracing a cut in the table with his finger. "There are certain rules of war that all men have come to accept. These rebels are stubborn, if nothing else, and if they do not crumble and break when we attack them, then perhaps they will deserve mercy. I do not believe that will happen - the *norteamericanos* are a selfish rabble. They do not march. They do not drill. They do not understand volley fire, or any of the tactics necessary for modern warfare. They do not respect their officers, and they follow them only at whim. When we attack them, they will splinter like cheap wood. They were not prepared for a siege - witness how poorly they planned for our approach. I have heard that their scouts saw us two days before we arrived in Béjar. How did they spend those days? Drinking? Dancing? Idiots! Were it not for Ramírez y Sesma "

"Ramírez y Sesma," I growled. "That timid little man will be the death of good Mexicans before this is over!"

"Yes, my friend, but he is powerful, and he has the ear of the President. He does not like you."

I laughed. "He would not dare to say it to my face!"

"No, he would not," Batres agreed. "You are a lion in battle, and he hates you for it."

I poured more mescal. My head was light, and the air tasted cold and sweet. "The *norteamericanos* will not allow us to win this war without their further involvement. They send their mercenaries now, but their armies will follow."

Batres nodded with vigor, and pounded the table with his fist. Bouncing glasses marked his every pause and point. "Yes, yes, yes, but we could solve that problem forever. Did you see how Travis and his men burned the grasslands before Béjar? As the Russians did to Napoleon in the Urals? Let us put the torch to this land and burn it back to desert. It will serve as a buffer between us and the *norteamericanos* who think the world was created for them to expand into. Let them find hundreds of miles of scorched earth. They will stay to the north, and leave us alone."

I downed my mescal and pushed the glass away. Batres tried to refill it, but I declined. "Enough," I said. "In moderation only." I took a deep breath of Texas air, and thought of the pecan trees and loose grass by the mill site. I could picture the roll and sway of the grass, tossed by the breeze like waves on a lake, bowing and brushing against the trunks of the trees. And the soil, now crisp and raw with winter, still hinting at the sweet, honeyed scent of spring.

It would be a shame to burn this land.

A courier entered *el Alamo* today, riding between the camp and the powder house. I wonder if His Excellency will counsel the commander that was so lacking in vigilance.[7]

We erected a battery within three hundred yards of the north wall today, and fired point-blank with nine-pound cannon. His Excellency once again presented himself on horseback, inspecting the batteries, within range of the long rifles, with no justification for the risk. Shots from the north wall whistled past, without effect. The men were greatly cheered by his presence, and *vivas* were sounded and seconded. For a moment, I saw His Excellency transformed, a gaunt *caballero*, a whirl of cape on a white horse, rearing up as if to strike the cold red sun with his steed's hooves. This dark angel would dare challenge death itself. We stood breathless, wondering in the wake of his velvet silhouette.

---

[7] The courier was James Bonham, returning with news of relief columns being formed in Gonzales. Bonham rode through Mexican lines at eleven o'clock in the morning, risking death to deliver his message of hope. He may have been the last man to enter the Alamo.

Yet this brave, sometimes foolish man, this last, best chance for the future of our Republic, insists on behaving as if he were a boy in a *colegio*.[8] His Excellency leaves me maddened and perplexed.

This evening the rebels attempted to do damage to the northern battery. Our riflemen drove them off easily, using British Baker rifles, which are not the equal of the *norteamericano* long rifles, but can be effective at more than two hundred yards. I encountered His Excellency shortly thereafter.

He was wide awake, and he paced the site with nervous energy. Caro followed in his wake, rubbing his sunken eyes with his shirt sleeve, trying to take down notes. I imagine that Caro had been asleep when the action took place, trying to catch a few moments of rest. The poor little man cannot enjoy much peace, not in his position. His Excellency fired his thoughts, one after another, his words puffing clouds of vapor into the night air. He stopped to shake his fist at the north wall of *el Alamo*, and boasted, "Now you see what it is like to face Mexican rifles!"

After Caro left to carry out one of the President's directives, His Excellency pulled me aside to whisper, "Urrea has taken the initiative in this campaign. It is of paramount importance that I achieve complete victory here immediately. I do not intend to sit and wait while Urrea wins this war."

---

[8] An institution for secondary education in nineteenth-century Mexico.

I sense that there will be no surrender now, and this sometimes great, and sometimes petty man will demand a payment in blood for the successes of his political rival.

## March 4, 1836. Béjar.

The rebels are erecting interior defenses, working with furious energy. We hear their hammer blows. It is brisk, not cold. Our bombardment began early this morning.

Late last night, the band played again to disrupt the pirates. They made a feeble effort to sound back at us with the sad moan of bagpipes, and the shriek of a fiddle, played like a chicken at slaughter. They cannot be sleeping well. They have lasted eleven days, I am astonished.

This afternoon, we held a council of war in His Excellency's quarters. The gravity of the proceedings demands a careful recounting. In attendance were His Excellency, Almonte, colonels Duque, Orisnuela, Romero, Salas, and Amat. Generals Cós and Ramírez y Sesma were there as well, sitting on either side of His Excellency like guard dogs. It was clear that His Excellency was fixed on the necessity of an assault. I did not see any point of trying to dissuade him, and in fact, there was no sentiment for continuing the siege, although the rebels must be close to surrender.

I cornered Almonte outside His Excellency's quarters before the start of the council. "If an assault is inevitable," I said, "then the method of attack must minimize our casualties. These rebels of Béjar have taken too many lives already. Bringas[9] has gone to expedite the placement of the twelve-pounders. They will arrive in a matter of days. Once in place, we can breach the wall with a half day of bombardment. Then the enemy will be helpless." Almonte shrugged his agreement, and then pulled free. "Let us go inside and see what our Commander has decided," he said.

His Excellency began by asking for comments. I took the opportunity to speak first. (None of the others seemed willing to commit themselves without hearing His Excellency's opinion, and so my initiative went unchallenged.) I spoke, conscious of the usual effect of my voice, compelling the others with sonorous tones and reasoned ideas. Almonte expressed his agreement with my point of view, sentiments that were echoed by Romero.

Then His Excellency and General Rameriz spoke in favor of an immediate assault, and then Almonte agreed with this as well![10] I stared at Almonte, astounded at this betrayal. How could the man agree with both points of view? Almonte would not return my gaze. He sat

---

[9] Colonel Juan Bringas.

[10] Both Almonte and de la Peña mention the meeting in their journals. Peña said that Almonte sided with Castrillón in his argument for the breach. Almonte claimed to side with Santa Anna in his own journal.

smiling, his eyes darting like minnows in a pond. His amiable face is a mask. Only he knows what he really thinks.

We concluded this phase of the discussion without any consensus. I note now, with some bitterness, that at the end of the council, some of those in attendance complained about His Excellency's opinions. The cowardly failure to argue for what they believe left His Excellency without proper advice. I expect that he will make his decision in solitude, as he has done for most of this campaign. We will all be at the mercy of that decision, thanks to those who are without backbone or principle. I reserve special disdain for Almonte in this regard. I thought the man better than that.

As we spoke, each officer glanced sideways at the President, trying to read his reaction. Few dared meet his gaze, the stern glare of an angry father.

One small surprise, Ramírez y Sesma and Cós offered a few token words about the wisdom of waiting for the siege cannon. Ramírez y Sesma sat quiet and pensive, poking at his uniform, studying his tiny fingernails. (He has the hands of a young girl.) When he spoke, he could barely be heard. Cós agreed, then clamped his lips shut like a virgin's legs. He gave the rebels his word not to return to Texas, and he broke it. His honor is clearly in question.

His Excellency yawned through the meeting, scratching his stomach, tapping his fingers in his lap, and otherwise showing disdain for the absence of a serious exchange of ideas, and yet, when anyone offered resistance to his dictates, he erupted, venting his rage. Such a moment occurred when the discussion turned to the treatment of prisoners.

Colonel Almonte opened the subject, arguing for the humane treatment of rebels who might wish to surrender. I was surprised to hear him say so, though I was glad of the opportunity to continue the discussion.

"The foreigners will be put to death," His Excellency pronounced. His voice was deep and clear, and had he been debating a point with Ramírez y Sesma, who squeaks and whines, there would have been no point in trying to disagree. I was speaking, however.

"There are certain standards that pertain to the conduct of war, standards which cannot be ignored," I said. "Humane treatment of prisoners does honor to victory, and the Republic must continue to found itself on honor and decency."

"I will have my Medina River," he answered me, his voice a low rumble, like thunder in an approaching storm. "Arredondo knew how to deal with traitors, and I have learned well the lessons of bloody rebellion."

"Breach the walls," I said. "Wellington lost 2,000 men battling through Ciudad Rodrigo."

"Then he showed them mercy," His Excellency shot back, "and so lost all the more men in Badajoz.[11] You have made my point."

"The point, my President, is what is right and what is wrong."

There was silence. For a moment, his dark eyes narrowed to hot black coals. "Thank you for your instruction, Castrillón. I am certain that we will all be the better for it." He stood and placed his hands flat on the table in front of him. "I neither ask for, nor give quarter. Does everyone in this room understand my decision on this matter? In a war on piracy, there are no prisoners. No prisoners."

The heads in the room bobbed, like oxen at a feed trough. I resolved to reintroduce the subject at a later time, when His Excellency and I were alone, to minimize his need to play to the audience of officers that serve him so poorly by their silence.

This evening, I rode out to the north battery, wondering what could be done to force a breach in that wall. The gun crews were frustrated by the quality of the powder. "It is little better than coal dust," one artillery sergeant told me. He showed me a keg that was exactly as he

---

[11] Castrillón and Santa Anna are arguing tactical points from Napoleon's wars in the Spanish peninsula.

described. The slow burn left roundshot dropping in front of the wall as often as not.

"Piss in it," I told him. He stared at me, and I realized that he was new to his vocation. The horse artillery brigade had been suspended two years earlier, and many of the men were novices. I smiled, and repeated myself. "When the urine dries, the powder will burn more quickly and evenly."

"Should I drink anything in particular, my General?" he asked, half afraid that I was having fun at his expense.

"Drink mescal, or even *pulque*," I laughed. "Tell them that General Castrillón said that the stronger the piss, the better the powder."[12]

## March 5, 1836. Béjar.

This afternoon, Caro came by with a copy of the battle orders. His Excellency has decided to attack tomorrow before dawn. I am more certain than ever that this is a mistake, and I will try to convince His Excellency of the merits of my argument this evening. I fear that we will squander many Mexican lives. The northern battery sits just two hundred yards from the north wall, and we still have not opened up a breach. Nine-pound cannon cannot do the job. Were we to wait a

---

[12] This was an old trick from before the Napoleonic era. In Europe, it was common for an artillery division to be followed by a beer wagon, especially for this purpose.

single day, two at the most, the siege guns would arrive, and we could take down the walls and save a hundred lives. I do not know if His Excellency still values my opinion, or support. I suppose I shall test that value today.

Colonel Duque and I are to attack from the northeast, arriving at the focal point of the bombardment. As I stated, I do not believe there will be a breach.

Ramírez y Sesma must be relieved to discover that he will patrol the perimeter of the field, cutting off any attempted escape by the rebels, thus personally avoiding most of the risk associated with the assault. This should remove his reservations about the attack.

The attack columns are to be provided with scaling ladders - crow bars, and axes. I have seen the men at work on the ladders, sticks tied with rawhide strips. I believe we will have more luck with the axes.

The batteries just ceased fire.

Good. If we must attack, let silence put these rebels to sleep. For twelve days we have fired on them, played music, shouted, and in general, sought to fray their nerves. Let them be lulled now. Let their fatigue pull them down, so that our men may advance unharmed when we storm the walls.

Word has come through Batres the rebels have offered to surrender. Travis sent a woman to His Excellency, acting as an intermediary. The rebels asked only for their lives, and offered to abandon the fort, and all arms and supplies.

His Excellency refused, demanding unconditional surrender. He is determined to take the life of every man in *el Alamo*, no matter what the cost. Travis will not succumb to this demand. He too is a stubborn man, as evidenced by our twelfth day of siege at this ridiculous place.

I do not believe that I will be successful in dissuading His Excellency.

The last hour of the day has come and gone. I visited His Excellency with a final, fruitless attempt at preventing the deaths that I am sure will come. Knowing that His Excellency sleeps irregularly now, I chose the late hour deliberately, so as to gain a solitary audience. Captain Urizza[13] was the sole witness to our unhappy conversation. The Commander sat nibbling chicken, dabbing at the corners of his mouth with a napkin, while his fingers became coated in grease. I stared with envy, and wondered how much the purveyors had charged His Excellency. Certainly, it was my own cook who prepared the meal. I had not eaten well again, and the chicken looked delicious.

---

[13]Captain Fernando Urizza.

"I have come to ask once again for your patience in securing *el Alamo*," I began. "Within days, perhaps hours, the twelve-pound cannon will arrive, and the rebels will be forced to surrender unconditionally. They will have no option. You will have your victory, and our men will not be killed needlessly."

He picked up a leg of chicken, and took a bite, chewing and pointing the leg at me. "I will have my victory, that much is certain."

"The victory need not cost Mexican lives."

He waved the leg at me, as if wagging a finger of disapproval. "What are the lives of soldiers more than so many chickens? I tell you, *el Alamo* must fall, and my orders must be obeyed at all hazards. You do still recall how to follow orders, do you not?"

I stood, and saluted. "I have always been at your service, Excellency." I could scarcely believe the affront.

He took another bite of chicken, stripping the leg to the bone. "We fight in a few hours, Castrillón. Go prepare yourself for the moment of battle." He dropped the bone, and grabbed another piece of chicken.

Every man must prepare for the terrible possibilities. No Mexican lives without dancing in the shadow of death. I may well perish in the battle to come. I regret having never married. I regret that I have sired

no sons. These are situations I intend to resolve should I survive this
campaign.

I grow maudlin. The enemy is weak, and disheartened. We will win
the battle in short order, and then move on. Well and good, I am sick
of Béjar!

On my way back to quarters, I came across Almonte. I could not
resist recalling how he had failed to present a consistent opinion at the
council on the 4th. I am sick at heart, and he noticed my irritation.

"But surely you understand, Castrillón," he said, his smile never
wavering. "His Excellency made clear through the course of the meeting
that he intended to attack. No argument could change his mind. I
agreed with you that we must wait for the cannon, but I did not wish to
anger His Excellency, and so -"

"And so you change horses in the center of the river."

His face became hard, and blank. He stared up at the sky, and
pointed. "Do you notice that the sky is clear, and the moon is nearly
full? His Excellency is quite angry with me for not informing him
ahead of time. We will make handsome targets in the moonlight, will
we not?" He started to walk on, and then glanced back. "On the
matter of taking prisoners, I did not waver. I put the whole of my
energy into that one small issue, and it did not help. This General of
ours keeps his own counsel."

That much is true. I too have expended a great deal of energy and concern, trying to force His Excellency to agree with me.

He has issued the orders. It is time to obey.

# Chapter

# 7

(Translator's note: The following entry was preceded by two false starts, paragraphs crossed out with slash marks and rendered illegible.)

## March 6, 1836. Béjar.

The battle for *el Alamo* is over, and we are victorious. The cost of that victory, both in men, and in the virtue of our cause, may some day be our undoing. It is late night, now, and I can hear the moans of the wounded through my window. I will continue to write through the night, careful to recall each detail of the day's events as they happened, lest I forget a single moment. I will spare no detail. Let judgment that falls be based on fact.

I took my place with Colonel Duque's men, northeast of the mission. The men were in place from 4 A.M. on, lying on the cold ground, waiting for the moon to wane. The night was clear and bitter with cold. The need for silence was obvious. The cessation of the bombardment lulled the enemy to sleep. For the first time in a dozen days, they could rest. If the attack went as planned, we would be scaling the walls before the rebels woke.

The Mexican soldier is a disciplined soldier. For hours we lay silent and still, waiting for the order to attack, with nothing but our thoughts to occupy us. We faced an amply fortified position. There were artillery pieces at all points on the walls, and our guns failed to breach those walls. Death sits at the side of every man, and this early morning, it leered at too many of us, waiting for the tick of a clock to take us away.

The walls of *el Alamo* were sharp, black angles that crouched in the brush. Beacon fires inside the fort shone upward, as if a lantern was tilted on its back, and the shutter hinge opened to the heavens. The moon colored the ground, cold grey and blue. A sharp wind cut across the grasses, and the men pressed close to the hard earth.

We made our peace with God. What remained was the preparation for the terrible moment of passage. In our hearts, we believed that fate was kind to present to us a death with meaning—in that death, our life would have meaning as well. Life without meaning "*es cádaver, es polvo, es sombra, es nada.*"[1] What we did not know was that our sacrifice would be demeaned, devalued by the foolish decisions of our Commander. In the end, where is the nobility in squandered life?

---

[1] "...cadaver, ashes, shadow, void." Castrillón is quoting a seventeenth century poet, Sor Juana Ines de la Cruz.

Many would not die, yet would suffer as much or more with wounds. Thought of lost limbs, and the searing, white-hot pain of battle wounds vexed us. In the silence, there was no reassurance. Fear is a solitary foe.

Still, we mortal souls strive to laugh at death, and to challenge it, and above all, to pray for the courage to emerge from the battle with honor intact. The insult to our men and country, sustained by the garrison at Béjar months ago, would at last be avenged. The foreigners, who by treachery and deceit had caused us to leave our winter homes and challenge death, would pay the supreme price for their folly.

These thoughts occupied my mind through the early hours of the morning. It is customary for a staff officer to view the battle from a distance, with the Commander. I expressed a desire to join the north column, and Santa Anna agreed with a disinterested wave of the hand.

Waiting for battle, I began to doze. It was a painful, jerking sleep that offered no rest. I woke myself several times, and drifted away again, reminding myself that whatever fate had in store for me, it would be over soon. I began to pray for the trumpet that would signal the attack.

At length it came, and I sat bolt upright, and began to stand before I was even fully aware. The sun glowed below the horizon. I could barely see the hands on my watch. It was half past five. I moved ahead, making good speed across the open grass. I whispered to myself, "*Adelante*"[2].

We moved as quickly as we could across the dark, uneven ground, trying not to stumble. The column was ordered to open fire while still a great distance from the north wall. To either side, we heard the discharge of Mexican rifles, and the thundering of *vivas* that spoiled the plan of surprise. I still hoped that we would reach the wall before the enemy was awake and alert, but cannon volleys cut short that dream, and replaced it with a nightmare.

I saw the yellow flash against the black wall, and heard the roar - a projectile passed inches from my ear, and punched a hole into the man behind me. A shriek tore through the column, and dozens of men were tossed back like sacks of corn. I turned to my left - the crimson rim of the new day lit the field. A hundred silhouettes scrambled against the morning sky. The field was already littered with bodies. This, from a single cannon blast.

As I ran, one of Colonel Duque's aides, Lieutenant de la Peña, grabbed me by the elbow, and shouted "Colonel Duque has been hit in the thigh! You must take command!"

I nodded, and pointed him to the north wall. Men raced past us, leaning forward against the rain of projectiles, as if moving ahead

---

[2] Forward.

through a storm. I tried to shout out, but the musket fire of the enemy drowned my voice with the furious roar of a waterfall. The first few moments were the worst. The rebels had stacked captured muskets, and fired four and five times each, with deadly accuracy. I saw a private take a shot in the center of the chest, exactly where the white straps of his uniform crossed, as if the "x" on his chest were a target. The attack faltered. I pitched myself forward, and by God's grace, reached the base of the wall. I immediately drew my pistol and looked up. The barrels of muskets and rifles poked over the rim of the wall, just four feet above my head, but there were no fandangos, or loopholes for the rebels to shoot through. One man leaned over the wall to discharge his double-barreled shotgun. I fired my pistol, and struck him in the head. He tumbled back, out of sight. No one could lean over the edge of the wall without exposing himself to lethal fire. If we could get the columns across the field, we could take advantage of the relative safety at the base of the wall.

I stood with my back to the limestone and adobe wall, and clutched my crucifix. Brass notes blared in the distance, as the trumpeters sounded the *Deguello*. Soldiers shouted, "*Viva Santa Anna!*" and "*Viva la Republica!*" as they ran. Cannon fire like lightning flashes lit the field, freezing single moments in time, as would a painting. I saw a man suspended in air, tossed by the blast of a cannon on the northwest corner. Men from the first column shifted from the west to the north, taking fire from both positions. Their men were completely out of formation, dodging foliage and bodies as they ran. Our column, which had arrived at the base of the wall first, was the first to falter. Our ladders were pinned under the bodies of dead comrades, or trampled and broken. There were no crowbars or axes to cut a handhold in the wall - they may have been dropped or pinned by the dead in the first rush.

The initial fury of the enemy fire had subsided, and many of the men of our column had reached the base of the wall. Others ran, stumbling in the dark, until they were turned around by the small contingents of cavalry that made up the rear guard of each column. They came back to us in subsequent waves. The column that attacked the east wall was thrown away in disorder, and had not yet joined us at the wall. The deadly fire of the rebels was to force that column north, resulting in the eventual massing of three of the four attack columns at the very point at which the rebels were most vulnerable.

Already, smoke from the cannon and muskets drifted over us, covering the field like a cloud. The shouts and cheers of the men were heartening, but foolhardy. In the early morning darkness, blanketed by smoke, the rebels were aided in their estimation of our position by our noisy enthusiasm, and we paid again and again with death. Still, the cheering continued, rolling across the grassland. I imagine that it caused the rebels great despair.

I tried to reload my pistol, frustrated in my efforts by the constant jostling of men trying to pin themselves closer to the wall. At last, I was reloaded, and sought to regain control of the men around me. I saw several men trying to place one of the flimsy ladders they had constructed. We were able to prop the thing against the wall, but it could not bear the weight of more than one man, and when several piled on, the wood splintered, and buckled, sending the men toppling down in a pile.

Some of the men would have turned back, but our gallant officers convinced them to resume the attack. The men from the column that skirted the east wall were beginning to arrive - desperate, sweating heroes who ran a gauntlet of fire to jam themselves against us. The whirl of soldiers at the base of the wall had grown, swelling with the combined men of three columns. The noise was deafening.

I had been sliding along the base of the wall, hoping to encounter someone with a crowbar, when I came upon a section that was well-battered by our cannon. The toll on the wall was obvious, since the rebels had tried to shore up the section with lumber. The bracing was crude and hastily erected, it may have been constructed just hours before the attack. As I stared at the work, it occurred to me that the answer to our dilemma was here.

Divine Providence had offered us the solution to the absence of a breach. We could not immediately exploit it, for at that same moment, our Commander lost faith in us, and sent in the reserves.

Santa Anna had been watching our slow progress. Perhaps he twisted his handkerchief, and dipped into his medicine box, afflicted with the stress of battle. The carefully laid plan of attack had been abandoned. Of the four columns, only ours held true to the original angle of attack. I discovered, after the battle, that the southern column was completely shattered, and reformed to attack the southwest corner, having blunted itself against the wooden palisade to the southeast, by the church. Cós had led his men into the northwest corner, rather than the west wall. I have already discussed Romero's column from the east. At Santa Anna's direction, Colonel Amat rushed forward, joined by the remaining members of the staff. The rebels, frustrated by their inability to fire on the targets below them without being instantly killed, had fresh opportunity to fire, and did so with great resolve. Worse, the reserves returned fire, shooting from the hip, as is the custom when discharging a musket with a .75-caliber ball. The first volley came waist-high across the grass, shearing our ranks. Men pressed closer into the wall, slamming me against the wooden bracing. I was stunned by the physical blows, as well as the realization that our own men were cutting us down.

When the reserves reached the wall, they added to the confusion. The jumbled mass of men shouted and screamed, jostling each other for position. From above came a new threat. The rebels, unable to lean over the wall lest they be shot instantly, were tilting their weapons over the edge and firing blind. This was a clever tactic, our men were compressed, and it was easy to strike an unseen target.

The north column was still mine to command. I directed some of the men to the wooden bracing at the base of the wall. In the absence of ladders, we needed a way up and over. (We could not fly, despite our President's expectations!) The bracing served as a crude ladder. Our men began to climb.

Those who went first died. Others followed. The rebels became desperate, and fought with incredible ferocity, with good reason. If we got inside the walls, they were finished. Their cannon would be silenced, and they would be slaughtered. Knowing this, they defended the position with every resource at their disposal, shooting, clubbing, and stabbing our men with bayonets as they ascended. Still we came on! I resolved to join the fray directly. General Amador pulled himself ahead of me, the veterans of so many wars were anxious to be the first to mount and hold the wall. My first attempt at the climb was cut short by a sergeant who shoved me aside, scrambling for a place on the bracing. Rank had no distinction in the swirl of men at the north wall.

When I succeeded in positioning myself, I began to breathe deeply, knowing that my moment had arrived. With just a few quick seconds of climbing, I pitched myself up onto the parapet. The men that had preceded me were bulling their way across the sandbagged wall, making room for others. I drew my pistol, and fired point-blank at a man just two yards from me, but the powder misfired. The rebel's rifle misfired as well, and the brief comedy ended when the rebel was struck dead by a bayonet thrust.

I knelt to tend to my weapon. The rebels had rammed dirt behind the wall where the bracing was erected, and it formed a ramp down into the plaza. Our men spilled over the top of the wall, and ran down inside. A new sound had been added to the cacophon - an alarm sounded, in honor of our entry. I glanced to my left, and saw rebels abandoning the cannon emplacement that had taken so many of our men's lives. To the right, I saw the men of Cós's column rising over the lip of the wall, with no one to stop them.

A handful of rebels, armed with muskets and bayonets, came rushing up the ramp in a belated effort to retake the wall. Our men dispatched them with ease. Some of the rebels retreated to their second line of defense, the rooms under the walls to the right and left of us.

Still others took a position in the open. My weapon reloaded, I joined

our soldiers as they flooded over the parapet and down into the plaza.

To my right, I saw soldiers streaming through a postern under the

northwest cannon emplacement. Others had climbed the walls, and

were dropping into the plaza from the rooftops of the rooms that lined

the west wall. The rebels were helpless against the tide of soldiers.

One Texan caught my notice. He was a tall, muscular blond who

fought with cool precision, firing carefully, and then moving back into

the plaza a few steps, giving ground only to reload. A few others,

frightened rabble, joined him in his stand, which lasted less than a

minute. At last, one of our men shot him in the leg. Unable to move,

he was helpless when the bayonets found him. The others were

dispatched without difficulty. I found out later, from Batres, that the

blond warrior was Travis, the commander of the fort.[3]

Darkness and smoke obscured what was happening at the far end of

the plaza. I am told that the fourth column, under the command of

---

[3] The man Castrillón saw was not Travis. According to his servant Joe,
Travis died at the north wall, with a single shot through the
forehead. Travis had dark hair, not blond. This description is
echoed by Enrique de la Peña in *With Santa Anna in Texas*. Peña
spent most of the battle running messages, writing his "diary" after
the fact, and may have used Castrillón's mistaken identification of
Travis in his account.

Colonel Morales, had taken the eighteen-pound cannon at the southwest corner, and was climbing into the plaza from that point.

As the rebels locked themselves into the barracks and supply rooms that ringed the interior of the plaza, they began to fire into the plaza at our soldiers through loopholes that they had prepared for that purpose.

As for our men, the exuberance of the charge had given way to angry determination. So many of us had fallen, and the real battle was just beginning.

I directed our men through the plaza. The sun had not yet risen, but fires inside the plaza lit our way. (The plaza is the large area indicated on the drawing.)[4] The few defenders who stayed in the open were swept away by our attack. In this, we relied on the bayonet as the principle weapon. Most of our men had discharged their weapons. Once the rebels were forced into hand-to-hand combat, they found themselves at a disadvantage. Those with rifles could not fix a bayonet to the end, and had to use the discharged weapon as a club. Those with bayoneted muskets were outnumbered, and overwhelmed. Those with knives had no reach. Their screams added fury to the sound of battle.

From the south gate came steady musket fire - it was the men of the fourth column, firing into the dark, once again striking our own men.

---

[4] Castrillón's original drawing of the Alamo was lost.

Some of our soldiers took shelter in the dry *acequia*[5] that ran from north to south along the west side of the plaza. Morales's men took refuge in the same trench at the south end of the plaza, when fire came from the small fort next to the wooden palisade.[6] This was the last open area of *el Alamo* to fall. Steady fire from the men in front of the church and from those on the roof of the two-story barracks kept our men pinned for a few minutes, but then these defenders fell too, and *el Alamo* plaza was ours.

The rebels still held the chapel and the rooms under the outer walls. I glanced at my watch - it was six o'clock. Most of the attack force was now inside *el Alamo*. Morales had been alerted to the dangers of random fire killing our own men, but shots continued to spray the plaza, and what control we had over our men was tenuous. Several circumstances conspired against us in this respect. The men had suffered grievous damage, and were anxious for revenge upon the remaining rebels. We had issued each man seven cartridges, an amazing amount considering the number of defenders. Now, our men reloaded, and fired at will, and for the next hour, the plaza was a slaughter pen.

[5] An irrigation ditch.

[6] The "small fort" that Castrillón refers to is the area that Crockett and his Tennessee volunteers were ordered to defend, bracketed by the wooden palisade and a low stone wall that ran parallel to the front of the church.

The air was alive with the hiss and spit of musket balls, as well as the steady spray of scrap metal from the cannon that still operated on the roof of the barracks, and the church itself.

The rebels had prepared for this phase of battle. The rooms that ringed the plaza were reinforced by earth-works, semi-circular bunkers, covered with hides. From these redoubts, the rebels poured fire on our men. Other rooms were fitted with loopholes, and the effect was the same. The nature of the battle had changed. The sudden chaotic rush that accompanied our frontal assault now gave way to methodical suppression. We were required to take these rooms one by one, and the process lasted most of an hour.

General Ampudia commandeered a cannon from the north wall, and rolled it down the dirt ramp, in order to use it, point-blank, on the rooms below the east wall. First round shot, followed by canister, and then our soldiers took the battered room by bayonet. In this fashion, we discovered that the defenders had taken out interior walls, or made passages from room to room, and that they were not necessarily trapped by our efforts.

On the west wall, the Aldama battalion concentrated its efforts on a small building near the northwest corner. I brought some of our men across the plaza to help clearing those two isolated rooms. Direction was difficult to give. As I shouted, the staccato gunfire was punctuated by the buck and roar of the larger pieces, and the men could only stare at me with blank faces. There was no point in repeating myself - I would have done as well to shout into the mouth of a cannon. Though I commanded the Toluca battalion, and three companies of riflemen from the San Luis, I could not make myself understood to more than a few men at any time. The lower ranked officers were particularly useless in this regard. I gave orders, but the maelstrom of screams and weapon fire swept my voice away, and I was reduced to hand signals, and a few key words.

I pressed against a stone arch, pistol cocked and ready. One of the men had an axe, and was flailing away at the door, which was braced and locked from the inside. I was safe from fire from within the room, but exposed to fire from the rooms across the plaza. (For the most part, this did not concern me, as men in the center of the plaza made better, more immediate targets.) The soldier with the axe crouched as he swung, ducking below the loophole that allowed fire from within the room. The plaza was filled with dust and white smoke from the muskets. I looked up - the sky was powder blue, and a thousand stars poked through. The crack of the axe on wood signaled the moment, the bar that latched the door had broken.

Our men slammed the door open, and fired blindly into the entryway. We raced into the dark room. I discharged my pistol, and struck a uniformed man dead center on the chest. The barrel flash lit the room - he pitched back, discharging his musket into the ceiling. The three other men in the room, all wearing uniforms, died by the bayonet.

Shots rang out from the adjacent room. The rebels had cut loopholes in the adobe and were firing at us. I dropped to the floor and rolled to the center wall, under the loopholes. Behind me, one of our soldiers was pinned against the far wall by rebel musket fire. Smoke and darkness blinded me, but I could hear him slide down the adobe wall and drop to the floor. Another soldier stumbled out of the room, cradling his head.

Moments later, our men broke into the other room. A few muffled shots were followed by the screams of the defenders. I dusted myself off, and went back outside. The door to the other room had been shattered open by the axe as well. Our men stayed inside longer than was necessary, and I could hear the rage of overly zealous soldiers as they stabbed the bodies repeatedly. It was a minor offense, justified under the stressful circumstances. Many of the rebels defending the building were wearing uniforms - proof of the *norteamericanos* interference.[7]

---

[7] The defenders mentioned here may well have been elements of the New Orleans Greys, regulars assigned to Travis command at the start of the conflict.

The thunder of cannon announced the destruction of another room across the plaza. The gunner followed roundshot with grape through an open door. White smoke shot into the entry, and billowed back out. Our men followed through the door, bayonets to the front.

On the roof of *El Cuartel*,[8] a drama played out before my eyes. One of the rebel's flags hung over the second story roof, an offense to all of us, and a series of *Zapadores* tried to take it. One by one, they were cut down. Then a young officer, who I later learned was José Maria Torres, raced across the rooftop. He tugged at the flagpole, defying the shots that whistled around him, exchanging the flag for the Mexican tricolor. He shook the pirate's colors, standing at the lip of the roof. We burst into enthusiastic shouts. I clapped and waved for this brave fellow, thinking, that young man is the real hero of Béjar! A private stood next to me, echoing my unspoken thoughts with words. Then a rifle shot dropped Torres. He died later in the day.

The rooms on the west wall fell, one by one. I am told that the rooms under the south wall fell the same way, by shot and steel. The sun peered over the horizon, and poor vision was not the limitation it had been, earlier in the battle. I could see our men struggling with the eighteen-pounder at the south wall. If they could make use of that piece, so much the better!

---

[8] "The Long Barracks."

I crossed the plaza, dodging shots, to join the Toluca in the battle over the barracks. Room by room, we took back what was ours, and the rebels were forced out of the L-shaped barracks, into *El Cuartel*. The rooms on the second story were riddled with gunfire, as a result of our attack against the men on the roof. Those rebels had taken too many of our lives without retribution, and the wrong was righted with emphasis.

The rooms below the second story were a different problem. The building sat with its back against the first rays of the morning sun. The entrance to the barracks faced away from the light. Inside the shadowy recesses, the advantages of the bayonet were minimized by poor visibility, and by awkward handling in close quarters. In the dark, the knife was supreme. Our men worked their way through the rooms that were battered by cannon, ensuring that no men would double back, but the methodical nature of the attack, and the slow movement of the cannon, ensured that much time would pass in the conquest of those rooms.

At one point, I moved in front of a room that we had cleared, and a rifle ball clipped my collar. I stepped to the side, pressing myself against the limestone walls, smelling the acrid stench of black powder all around me. Others ran into the room, discovering a man in the corner who had escaped notice simply by standing still in the blackness. They pitched him on their bayonets, causing great commotion with their screams and his.

When it was apparent to all that we would be the victor, some rebels tried to run. I am told that men at the palisade next to the church hopped the earth-and-picket fence, and tried to escape past the abatis[9] and into the open fields. Ramírez y Sesma, who was much too precious to risk frontal assault of an enemy position, was stationed with his cavalry to intercept such an escape attempt. (Santa Anna boasted to us that all who tried to run were slain, but that is simply not true. A lieutenant was killed by one of the rebels, and in the ensuing mêlée, two men got away, one on the Lieutenant's horse. A woman from Béjar spotted one of the men hiding under a bridge. Soldiers were summoned, and he was shot. It was believed that the other was badly wounded, but he was not apprehended.)[10]

From inside one of the rooms on the east wall, I saw a bayonet thrust out over the top of the barricade, adorned with a dirty piece of cloth. From inside, we heard cries for mercy, as if, having sated their

---

[9] An abatis is a defensive barrier, made in this case by the sharpened limbs of felled trees.

[10] Some historians believe that Henry Warnell was able to escape to his family in Dimmit's Landing. It is thought that he died of his wounds shortly after the battle. Texas land records lend credibility to this account. Could Warnell be the man to which Castrillón referred?

taste for killing, the rebels could call on our honor to save them. The sergeant closest to the door straightened, his smoke-blackened face weary with battle. He motioned to his men, and then entered the room, trusting the request for truce.

The flag was a ruse. Once inside, the pirates fell upon the sergeant and his men, knifing them, killing all three. Our furious response was immediate and just. We redoubled our efforts to take the room, and when we did, the five men sequestered inside were torn apart by the tips of our bayonets.

Our men could scarcely be restrained. They fired into the rooms of *El Cuartel* and burst into each. It was here, in the dark, that the order to spare no one cost us most dearly. Some of the rebels begged for their lives as we took them, but most of the rebels were resolved to fight to the death, wishing only to inflict loss on our army. Unlike those who begged, these rebels deserved our mercy. Instead, they fought to the death, theirs and ours, and the result was a shower of blood.

As our men poured into the rooms, they blindly discharged their weapons against both friend and foe. In some instances, the firing continued for minutes after the last rebel had perished, and these outbursts of gunfire continued to break out at different points around the plaza. In the end, we trusted only the cannon to clear the rooms.

By now, many of the rebels had run out of ammunition, and the greater part of the damage to us was being done by our own men. We needed to stop firing, and bring order to the assault. Earlier, Cós had enlisted a *Zapadores* bugler named Tamayo to sound cease fire, but the signal could not prevail above the noise of weapon discharge.

I followed *El Cuartel* to the corner, where Morales had dragged the eighteen-pounder down from the southwest corner. He positioned it to fire into the entryway of the church itself. They fired round after round straight back through the nave of the old limestone chapel. Return fire, brisk at first, eventually ceased. White smoke hovered around us, as if a giant cloud had dropped down into the plaza. Soldiers from the Matamoros and the Jimenez, led by Colonel Juan Morales, entered the building, and killed the few remaining rebels. I followed the fifty or so men into the church, and witnessed the death of one rebel gunner. The man jumped from the elevated gun platform at the rear of the church, carrying his young son. Some of our men fired, and both the man and his son perished, either from the fall or from our fire. I was later told that the gunner was named Dickinson.[11]

---

[11] The man was not Dickinson. He was probably Anthony Wolfe, who had two boys, one aged 11, and the other aged 12.

Our men fired into one dark room repeatedly, and when someone produced a lantern, we found a rebel, still in his bed, shot through the chest and head several times. Blood splattered the wall behind him. One soldier told me that the man's face was so white with fear, that our men thought him a ghost.[12]

After freeing a captured soldier,[13] we found the women and children in the small stone room to the right, just inside the church entry. Some rebels tried to hide with them. Two were shot, and a third was bayoneted as he begged for mercy. A young boy was bayoneted as well,[14] and it was now clear that the lust for battle had exceeded our ability to control the men. The last rebel was raised and lowered on our bayonets, as was the young boy, who cried piteously. I ordered the torture to stop immediately. I thank God for my voice, which cut through the screams and gunfire, before our men committed the atrocity of killing the little girl and her mother! The boy died in convulsions, as did the rebel gunner.

---

[12] Judged by Castrillón's description, the man on the bed may have been Jim Bowie.

[13] This passage probably refers to a Mexican deserter, Brigido Guerrrero, who had joined the Alamo defenders. When captured, he convinced the Mexicans that he had been held against his will. He survived the siege and later received land for his residency in Texas and a pension for his role in the Texas Revolution.

[14] Probably the other son of Anthony Wolf.

Colonel Morales forced his way into the room, calling out for the woman, who turned out to be Mrs. Dickinson. We had been informed of the presence of women and children by our spies, but there was no way of knowing in advance where the rebels would sequester them. Morales was distressed to find that Mrs. Dickinson had taken a musket ball in the calf during the melee.

Assured that Morales would see to the safety of the survivors, I left the church, and stepped back out into the plaza. The sun was up. Golden beams from the back of the church cut through the dense smoke of battle. Random shots were still being fired, but the fighting was over.

As I walked, I saw the signs of battle everywhere. Men lay in heaps, burned by fires, weapons scattered. Some of our men stripped the bodies of the rebels, a shameful act which must be forgiven. How many of our men wear their jackets next to their chest, instead of a shirt? How many walk barefoot through the plaza?

The large white bodies that littered the scene of devastation were contrasted by black and bloody faces. Torn limbs and torn uniforms smoldered in the fires. The stench turned my stomach. The cries of the wounded and the dying filled the air. I began to look for familiar faces, hoping to find those I recognized on the living, not the dead. It was in this apprehensive state that my attention was drawn by a sudden rebirth of gunfire at the base of *El Cuartel*. I rushed into the rooms, scrambling over the earthworks that provided the rebels cover. In a rear room, shrouded in darkness, a small pocket of rebels were still fighting. They had no more ammunition, but each time our soldiers attempted to enter the room, someone just inside the door clubbed with his rifle, injuring another soldier. Two men lay dead in the doorway, one with knife wounds. Our men fired into the room repeatedly, but the rebels inside stayed pressed against the walls, out of danger. The door was too narrow for more than one of our men to go through at a time.

As I approached, one of our men was trying to angle his musket in, hoping for a shot at the one who guarded the door. He fired, to no avail, and his shot was answered tenfold by other soldiers in the plaza. I ordered the soldiers back.

I stood in front of the door, and called in to the rebels. "Lay down your weapons, brave soldiers," I said. "The time for killing is over." My English is poor, and so I gestured as well, holding my hand out into the doorway. "I offer you my protection." A soldier jostled me from behind. I turned and froze him in place with a single glance. He backed away, looking down. "These men are prisoners," I said. "You will respect my wishes."

I turned back to the doorway. "Come with me," I said. "I will present you to the commander, Santa Anna, and you will be spared."

There were whispers from inside, and then silence. I waited. Just as my patience was ending, they began to file out. Six men and a boy came out, the latter no more than thirteen or fourteen years old. They were dirty, sweat-soaked, and frightened. One man was armed with a knife, another with the leg of a table. They dropped these weapons at my feet, and stood, awaiting my instructions.

Last to leave the room was an older man, carrying the shattered barrel of a rifle. He was tall, though not as tall as I, and nearly my age, from the sight of him. He stood next to the boy, draping an arm around the boy's shoulders. This *anciano*[15] had a certain noble melancholy to him. He had fought a good fight, and was resigned to death. He nodded, and I bowed slightly. He introduced himself, and I returned the courtesy. I pointed the way to the plaza, and the surviving rebels followed me into the sun.

As I walked, I glanced at my watch. It was after seven. A slight breeze had cleared some of the smoke from the plaza. I led the survivors toward the south gate.

As we crossed the edge of barracks, I saw that the President had entered the fort, and was standing by the entrance to the church. Ramírez y Sesma and some of the staff officers were accompanying his

---

[15] "ancient one"

inspection of the battle site. I motioned for the rebels to follow. On the way, we attracted a crowd of onlookers - the soldiers could not believe that any rebels had survived the fray.

As we walked, the older man called (Crockett)[16] spoke, trying to convince me of the fine decision I had made. "I am a foreign national," he confided. "I did not believe that my neutrality would be respected, and I was forced to fight -"

"Is that right?" I asked. I stared at him, and he gave me a sad smile. I understood that he was trying to talk his way out of trouble.

I led the prisoners before our President, and bowed gracefully, offering them for his decision. Santa Anna turned. He wore a simple, unpretentious battlefield uniform. I believed that he would recant his order. Mexico is a civilized nation, and our soldiers are valiant and honorable. "Your Excellency," I said, "I present to you these brave prisoners of war. Their courage merits our gallantry."

The Presidents eyes were half-closed in the glare of the morning sun. "Who gave the order to take prisoners?" he asked.

"Your Excellency," I whispered, stepping closer to speak candidly. As I spoke, Ramírez y Sesma leaned in, hoping to hear more clearly. "The

---

[16] Castrillón wrote "Cockran." The Mexicans had a terrible time with Crockett's name. José Juan Sánchez Navarro called him "Cochran." Rafael Soldana called him "Kwockey."

one is just a boy, and the old man is this Crockett we've all heard about. You can certainly use these men to your advantage -"

"By what right do you ignore my orders, Castrillón?" he asked. I glanced back at the rebels, and in that one instant, my eyes met with the eyes of the one called Crockett. A hard truth passed between us, and the man straightened up, and folded his arms in front of his chest. He knew what was about to occur, and he glared at Santa Anna with defiance. I shall never forget that look.

The President turned his back on me. "Kill them," he ordered. The officers of the staff leapt forward, pulling their swords. The young boy screamed, and the others stepped back. Crockett drew the boy to him, stepping in front as if to shield him. It was no use. Officers who had avoided battle, staying close to Santa Anna during the fight, sought to perform acts of "bravery" against these unfortunates. They leapt in for the kill against the disarmed.

Ramírez y Sesma was particularly ferocious, anxious to defend the Republic with saber thrusts to the shoulders and thighs of one rebel. The man was not killed outright, but was instead, tortured in a most offensive manner.

I stared in stark horror. The rebels lashed back, swinging fists, shrieking at the outrage of the execution. Crockett and the young boy were pinned to the dirt with a dozen blades.

As I turned away, my eyes met the President's. We understand each other quite well. We are no longer friends.

I had been humiliated by our General in front of his staff. I returned to my quarters, there being no other action left to me.

I would have slept.

I had not rested in more than a day, and I knew that I was tired, but I could not remove the pictures of carnage from my mind. I tossed and turned on my straw bunk, and finally threw my blanket aside. I decided to walk through Béjar. I was careful not to encounter our General. I could not bear to see him again today.

It was late afternoon. A most unpleasant smell drifted through the streets - Santa Anna had ordered the rebel dead to be burned rather than buried.

As I walked, I came upon Sergeant Sánchez Navarro. He stopped me, clutching my cape with his questioning hand. "Do you recall our conversation so many weeks ago?" he asked. His eyes were shot red, and he was nearly weeping. "What do you think now, my general?"

"Who can say?" I mumbled, and pushed on. I had told Sánchez Navarro that Cós had been beaten by pirates, and that we would march over them without trouble. Now I fear for the success of the campaign, and even the very survival of the army.

The streets of Béjar are alive with whispers. I have heard the muttering of our men, wondering why it was necessary for our victory to be so costly, and why our President desires that his glory be sealed in blood. I know this if all of our victories must cost as much, then we dare not win this campaign.

# Chapter
# 8

**March 9, 1836. Béjar.**

I left my quarters today. The stench of burned bodies has lessened.

Filisola arrived, and signed the official report of the battle for *el Alamo*. I am curious how this Italian can count the bodies of Mexicans killed. There were so many, they threw some into the river, and floated them away, bloated blue and red bundles without a proper grave. I saw a body cling to the bank, like a baby at a mother's breast, it's legs dangling out behind it in the current. How many dead? The official report claimed seventy dead, and nearly 300 wounded. If these wishful totals reflect the truth, then why were Mexican bodies dumped in the river? Why were they not all buried? Surely we could have offered proper rites to seventy men!

Worse, there are no medicines. A there is a shortage of gauze. Not enough bandages. This catastrophe does not affect our Commander, of course. When a call went out for officers to donate their linens for bandages, Santa Anna refused, preferring to keep his wardrobe intact!

There are no straw mattresses, or even blankets. The wounded will die, as they have been dying for three days, and when the final count is made, the victims of Santa Anna's assault will number in the hundreds. Five hundred. Six hundred. The mind spins and closes shut.

How would I have acted differently, had I known? Would I have demanded that Santa Anna postpone his attack, and await the siege guns? Would I have insisted that we accept the offered surrender of the rebel garrison? Would I have pressed the issue, to the point of insubordination? I do not know the answers to these questions. I am shocked into disbelief. I can only record the outrages I have witnessed.

I walked through Béjar, staring at the wounded stacked in the streets. How can so many be maimed and mutilated? The rebels fired bits of metal refuse at us, and left us with shattered bones, and infected punctures. We know enough about the medical sciences to remedy these insults to the flesh, but we were not prepared. There are not enough surgeons.

From a distance of a few houses, I saw Santa Anna visiting the wounded men, and some of them were cheered by the President's arrival. I watched him move, stiff and mannered, offering a curt bow or nod to the tortured. I suppose that Santa Anna believes that his mere presence can offer a remedy to the pain of battle. At the most, his visits deflect criticism. The men are depressed, and many of the insults and complaints are deferred to Tornel[1].

Not everyone is unhappy with the turn of events. Fate grins like an idiot at the merchants, who have now fully realized their speculative potential. A tent has been set up by the President's quarters, and is called the "President's Tent." Goods sell for many times their real market value. A portion of flour, or a portion of corn costs our soldiers three pesos. A *piloncillo*[2] costs a peso. Pecans, harvested from trees here in Béjar, cost a *medio real* for a few dozen. It is said that only Ramírez y Sesma eats well in Béjar.

Incriminating rumors abound - it is said that since the provisioner general is Santa Anna's brother-in-law,[3] some of the money ends up in the President's pockets. This last outrage, if true, would be the blackest stain on his already darkened heart.

I had eaten only a few bites in several days, so I endeavored to purchase a small meal. I would have been satisfied with some meat and tortillas, but even this was not available. I bought pecans, and a small, sour loaf of bread. It is not well that I have neglected my physical

---

[1] José María Tornel, the Mexican secretary of war.

[2] A small, cone-shaped pastry made of brown sugar.

[3] Castrillón is referring to Ricardo Dromundo.

needs.  I cannot afford to get sick, not when there is no doctor, perhaps within a hundred leagues.

Wounded men still able to walk wandered past me, searching for comfort.  Others lay in the streets, waiting for a miracle.

For many, the suffering was mortal.  I stopped in front of one soldier who suffered from chest and shoulder wounds, not knowing why at first.  He had wedged himself against the corner of a building, and the afternoon sun angled over the rooftops, into his eyes.  His uniform was caked with dried blood.  His black hair was plastered to the back of his neck.  I wondered how long it had been since he had a drink of water.  It was only then that I recognized him, it was the private who had survived the storm with me, on the march north from Saltillo.

I tapped his good shoulder, wondering if he was dead.  He groaned, and opened his eyes into slits.  "Can you hear me?" I asked.  No answer.  "Can I get you anything?"

A conscript passed by.  I grabbed him and asked, "Who is tending these men?"  He shrugged, frightened.  "Fetch water for this man," I said.  The conscript bowed, and hurried away.

I crouched beside the Indian.  His mouth dropped open.  His breath smelled of old teeth.  He whispered *"Por fin, descansaré."*[4]  A thin stream of brown trickled from the corner of his mouth.  He was spitting up

---

[4] "At last, I will rest."

blood and saliva. I stood up. There was nothing more that I could do for him, he was going to die.

As I write, I wonder what I will do now. I have spent days resting in my room, considering what has happened. That is over. I am a man of action, and I must not let these events shape the destiny of my country without answering back for all that is good, and all that is right with Mexico. Duty demands a response.

## March 11, 1836. Béjar.

The rest of the army has arrived, and on cue, Ramírez y Sesma has moved on. The President will divide his forces into three parts, one each heading for Goliad, Gonzales, and San Felipe. I conversed with Santa Anna this afternoon. It was inevitable.

The President was up early, not his recent habit, and he was highly agitated. "Castrillón!" he shouted, as he strode into my quarters. "I would have a word with you." Sweat rolled down his neck, though it was barely an hour past sunrise, with a morning chill still in the air. His blue uniform collar was stiff with grime.

I was sitting at my table, pushing a fork at some beans and corn. I did not stand up.

"I did not know you were eating," he said. "Go ahead, go ahead. Do you have a moment?" He waited, his hands at his side, until I nodded. "It looks delicious," he said, frowning at my small plate of vegetables. "But surely you can afford something more sustaining, my friend? Something with some meat in it? You cannot maintain your health with a ration of beans."

I took another forkful.

"I assume that you are feeling better. You look fit," he continued, pretending that my absence from his presence was due to illness. He held out a sheaf of letters. When I did not take them from him, he set them on the table next to my meal. "Sr. Urrea sends me dispatches daily. His successes do honor to the Republic."

"He is a fine commander," I said between bites.

"Yes, he is. If you read these letters, you will note that he anticipates further successes. His tone is... " He paused, as if to search for the exact word. "He is eager, perhaps anxious. I believe he would prefer to win the campaign single-handed." He paused again. "Do you enjoy cockfights, Castrillón?"

"No, I never acquired the taste."

"To your loss. Much can be learned from observing. Imagine a champion, bred from the finest stock, raised and trained, with an instinct for the kill. Such a champion would be eager to fight every opponent, and leave none for the-" He glanced out the window, suddenly distracted. "You should eat some meat, Castrillón." He wiped at his nose with his thumb and index finger. "At any rate, such a champion has no sense of its limitations."

"You are suggesting that Sr. Urrea needs a rest," I said.

Santa Anna shrugged. "He may well be capable of finishing both Fannin and Houston, but he is too valuable to risk. If he fails, he would deprive the invasion of its right flank, the third tine of my trident."

"Victory has its risks as well," I noted. I flipped through the dispatches. "His defeat of the Grant party[5] has put him in position to take Goliad."

"And if he takes Goliad," Santa Anna said, "the war will be over." His face softened for a moment. "An old soldier like you might be surprised to learn that your Commander has occasional doubts, occasional fears."

I weighed my words carefully. "Your Excellency, you have won a great victory here in Béjar."

"Yes, I know, I know," he said, pacing the floor. As he spoke, he waved his hands through the air as if he were swimming. "But if Goliad falls, there will be Sam Houston, and his army will dissolve when the news of Goliad reaches them. What is your advice, Castrillón? Be candid!"

---

[5] On March 2, 1836, Urrea's lancers met and destroyed a Texan party under the command of Colonel James Grant.

I scratched my chin, as if I were considering options. In truth, I was trying not to laugh. He was like a little boy in a pool, over his head, afraid of drowning, calling for a rope. Was this the great man to whom I dedicated my career?

Still, I had to answer my illustrious *Caudillo*. "Your Excellency, it is my opinion that you should travel back to Mexico City, and accept the thanks and adulation of your grateful people. While Urrea and the rest of us tidy up the pockets of resistance, you can shoulder the role of conqueror. Assign Urrea to police Texas, and burn it to the ground if you wish. By the time he returns, there will be other wars for the people to cheer."

Santa Anna stared at me, his mouth slightly open. His lips were wet, and he licked them once. I thought for a moment that he could read my thoughts, and I felt myself about to blush. Then he pulled himself up, and straightened his shoulders. "Thank you for your opinion," he said, his voice once again imperious. "I will consider it, along with others, of course. Good day."

I knew then that he would do exactly as I suggested. True command might be more than he could muster, but politics were his forte. I had offered him a political solution.

It is a denouement I can live with.

## March 12, 1836. Béjar, always and forever Béjar!

Today, Santa Anna reviewed the troops in the square. I was reminded of Saltillo, a hundred years ago, or was it only ten weeks? So much has changed.

The men are tired, and dirty, and discouraged. When I was a boy, I saw a string-puppet theater. I was amused by the lilting, jerky motion of the figures. Today I watched our soldiers parade past using the same skeletal motions, and I am not amused.

The wounded that have not yet died were not cheered by the display. Did the President really believe that they would be? Can a man aching with shattered bones or burning with infection care about parades?

I stayed away from Santa Anna, but found no want of conversation. Members of the staff came to me, one by one, expressing their dismay over the turn of events.

First was my old friend Batres. He drifted through the crowd, as if he was unsure of his destination. I stood still, waiting for him to make his approach. "Batres," I said. "I have been wondering if I would grow old and die before you arrived."

"You are already quite old, Castrillón," he wheezed. "Did you eat well today?" Some of the staff ate fish for midday meal.

"Yes, I have always been fond of that manner of cooking," I told him.

"I have been worried about you, Castrillón," he said. I waved him off, but he continued. "The business in *el Alamo* was regrettable. The officers and the men were angered. Our president is," and here his voice dropped to a hiss, "a barbarian. If I were a younger man, I would protest most vehemently."

I stood still, my head cocked in his direction.

"I am tired, my friend. At night, the cold works into my bones and stays there. It turns my joints to ice." His shoulders sank down into his chest. Each shallow breath rattled in his throat. "The campaign will end soon," he continued. "When it does, I will rejoice. I am too old for the soldier's life." He paused, and cleared his throat. "What will you do when the rebels are defeated?"

"I am not certain," I told him. "Retirement holds certain inducements. Perhaps I will marry a slender girl and fatten her with good food and children."

His smile was a whisper of his old grin. Batres has become melancholy in his dotage. "You are a soldier, Castrillón. If you married, your wife would soon beg you to go to war. Besides, you are our President's conscience. Without you, he has no wheel-break."

"I have no particular influence with Santa Anna," I said.

"Not so, my friend. His Excellency walks with faint steps, waiting for you to forgive his behavior. Almonte told me as much."

"It is not for me to forgive the President. If he is besieged by guilt, perhaps he should petition the men who lay dying in the streets of Béjar."

Batres shrugged. "It is true. The battle for *el Alamo* was unnecessarily costly. Still, the rebels lost more than 250 men, I counted them myself."

I poked Batres in the shoulder and smiled. "You must have counted legs then, old friend.[6]"

"Perhaps," he sighed.

Later, Cós came by, wondering if I was over my "illness." I assured him that I was quite well. "Good, good," he cooed, plucking at his mustache, which had sprouted disorder over the past few weeks. "Tell me, Castrillón. Is it true that one of the rebels you tried to save was the politician, David Crockett?"

I shrugged. "He said as much."

---

[6] Castrillón chides Batres for inflating the number of defenders. Estimates of the number of dead defenders go from 182 (the figure accepted by most textbooks) to 253 (reported by Peña). The actual number was probably somewhere in the middle. The roster reports from Travis do not include wounded men. The Texans probably lost between 200 and 210 men.

"I understand that he claimed to be a foreign neutral."[7]

"There is no such thing as a foreign neutral," I said.

He agreed. "I wonder how we will fare when we head north?" he asked.

My conversation with Sr. Batres had soured me. I said, "Surely you are not afraid of these Texans, Cós, with the stink of their corpses still in the air."

He stiffened, as if he'd been slapped. "I ran into the mouths of cannon, as did you, Castrillón. Simple courtesy requires that you remember this."

I agreed, ashamed by my manners. I offered an apology, and moved on. I do not like Cós, and I will never like him, but the anger I felt at his shortcomings as an officer has disappeared in the face of the greater transgressions of our Commander. Cós is arrogant and inept, an irritating combination, but he does not hold the fate of our country in his hands.

---

[7] After San Jacinto, Cós was interviewed by a Dr. George M. Patrick, who related the substance of the conversation to the noted Texas historian William Zuber. Cós described finding Davy Crockett, well dressed and articulate, waiting in a barracks room. Crockett proclaimed his neutrality, then Cós brought him to Santa Anna, who had him killed. It is likely that Cós was offering a fabrication of half-truth, staff gossip, and self-promotion. The story may have been based, in part, on Castrillón's conversation with Cós.

Later still, Caro slid by. "His Excellency has decided to go back to Mexico City," he offered. "There is nothing more to do here in Texas. Urrea can clean up the mess, like a good servant boy."

"Urrea is a fine commander," I said, "as are all the members of the President's staff."

Caro snorted. "You are a talented man, Castrillón, and a humble one. Perhaps your humility explains your failure to secure an independent command. Perhaps if you had married one of the President's sisters -"

I laughed. Men trudged by, with mud-splattered feet in sandals, some worn and falling away. "What do you want, Caro?" I asked.

"Nothing beyond your opinion. Do you think that the campaign nears completion?"

"I suppose so."

He frowned, and his eyes pinched together. "Houston has a thousand men waiting for us "

"Houston has a rabble," I snapped. "The rebels have no government, so they have no direction. They can be no real threat."

"Perhaps you are right," Caro whined, meaning that he disagreed. My patience with conversation had ended, and I made an abrupt exit.

## March 15, 1836. Béjar.

News arrived from Washington.[8] The Texans have declared independence, and formed their own government. I derided these same rebels just yesterday. So much for my powers of prognostication. (I am certain that Caro has already forgotten my words. He has His Excellency to divert his attention.)

More troops have marched for Goliad. That battle may be over as I write. I pray that it is so. Sr. Urrea is a professional, and he takes fewer casualties than Santa Anna. One more victory may yet finish the campaign, and save us from further waste.

I look from the window of my quarters, and breathe a prayer, while the fine young men of Mexico walk the streets like so many of Santa Anna's chicken legs, ready to be devoured.

## March 16, 1836. Béjar.

We have set to the task of keeping the men busy. I had occasion to watch a group of men on such a work detail today, and the display was unsettling.

The men are unkept, and slovenly. They are sullen bags of bone, with uniforms so beyond care that they hang like nets of stitch and patch. Dust has worked into their pores, and caked on their faces.

---

[8] Washington-on-the-Brazos, the acting capital of Texas.

One conscript (not an Indian, perhaps a jailhouse recruit), sat down, cursing openly in front of his officer. He pulled a sliver of corncake from his pocket and began to stuff bits of it into his swollen mouth. As I watched him, he met my gaze with a malevolent insolence that angered and dismayed me. I asked the lieutenant what he intended to do. "What can I do?" he whispered bitterly. "Look at these men! They are two hundred leagues from their homes, and they no longer care about the Republic."

"It appears that the Republic does not care for them," I answered. "Do your men eat well, or do they all nibble at corncake like mice?"

The lieutenant scowled and looked away. It is one thing to wonder at such insolence in a conscript. It is another to tolerate it in the behavior of an officer. "These men have no food!" I snapped. "How long will they work without sustenance? Until they drop?"

"No man can afford the prices charged for a simple meal!" the lieutenant moaned.

I pulled money from my wallet, and shoved it into the lieutenant's hand. He stared at me as if I had gone mad. Perhaps. I acted out of anger, not charity. I am a staff officer, and I do not have the resources to make a difference. "Buy these men a meal, sir. Tell them that the Republic cares whether they live or die."

"Of course, General," he whispered, backing away. I imagine that the moment I was gone, the money found its way into his pocket. As I stood watching, other soldiers sat down, removing their *shakos* and wiping the sweat from their dirty faces. This was not the army that left Saltillo. The soldiers in Saltillo had full bellies, and they believed that there were enough surgeons and chaplains in attendance to offer the physical and spiritual comforts due to men who risked their lives for their country. These men are whipped dogs waiting for a defeat to latch on to.

But the malaise that afflicts our men goes deeper than just an empty belly. I believe that we have surrendered the higher moral ground by our behavior here in Béjar. We came north to redress wrongs that were done to our Republic by foreign interlopers. We were right to do so, and justice was our ally. You cannot ask men to die for an unjust cause, they will not offer the ultimate sacrifice without the opportunity to serve a higher good. That is why our army has consistently defeated the rebels in the field. Our cause is honorable.

When we massacred the rebels here in Béjar, we ignored the virtues of mercy, and honor. That is why I am haunted by the image of Crockett, an old man, arms folded, staring with defiance, waiting for his execution. That man was a pirate, and we have made a martyr of him.

## March 17, 1836. Béjar.

Almonte visited me outside *el Alamo* this morning. I had gone to see the funeral pyres of the rebels, southeast of the mission. The ruined old church made a sad background for the pyres. Wood and bones, burned to ash, lay in charred piles, to be shuffled by the wind. The ground around the piles had soaked to black with the grease of burned corpses. Almonte watched in silence for some time, and then approached me. "The President is angry over Urrea's correspondence," he said. "He requests permission to chase Houston, and end the campaign. It is the President's position that the campaign is over. Barragan's death has complicated the issue, the President is afraid that Bustamante will use the death to his advantage.[9] Now Urrea would steal the last glory from our very glory-conscious leader. Until yesterday, I believe that he was predisposed to return to Mexico City and allow Filisola to finish things here in Texas."

I volunteered nothing.

---

[9] Miguel Barragan was Santa Anna's vice-president, acting as president in Santa Anna's absence. The death of Barragan weakened Santa Anna political position back in Mexico City. Anastasio Bustamante, the new acting president, issued a decree that reversed Santa Anna's policy of "no quarter." Bustamante was a political rival, once the president of Mexico, who was in fact to serve as president again after Santa Anna's defeat at San Jacinto.

"The President is outraged at the language of Urrea's communications. The young general has a haughty pen."

"What do you want of me, Almonte?" I asked. "I cannot influence the President."

"You hold yourself in low esteem, Castrillón," Almonte said. "In times of great turmoil, we must all stand together for God and the Republic."

I smiled. I do not think it was a friendly smile.

Almonte cleared his throat. "Urrea would go after Houston alone. The President will not allow that to happen. The men, on the other hand, are demoralized. It is a dangerous situation."

"Are you saying that Santa Anna should stay or go?"

"The President will decide to stay," Almonte said. "We will march deeper into this country. I am concerned with the outcome. It would be a disaster to lose this campaign. Our President will need all of our combined experience -"

"The President keeps his own counsel," I said.

"That is true, Castrillón," he said. His smile disappeared. "It is also true that the men need to see a staff united in its support of the President, available to steer him from the worst of his decisions. Santa Anna must triumph here in Texas. He must! Do you not recall what the years of civil war have been like? Have you forgotten the sad parade of tyrants that bled our country? You brood over the few hundred men who suffered here in Béjar. What about the thousands who will suffer if we plunge into another cockfight between our politicians? Would you see our President fail?"

I stared at the grease-blackened ground. "If the *norteamericanos* defeat us, then we will deserve our fate."

Almonte measured his words carefully. "You cannot afford to sulk in your quarters while your country courts disaster "

"I have always done my duty," I snapped. "You watch over your President, if you like. I am a soldier, not a wet-nurse."

I started away, but I came back, like a piece of wood at the edge of a lake, dragged back and forth by the waves. "And has it occurred to you, my friend," I spat, "that our sense of duty permits His Excellency greater and more astounding abuses of the country we serve? Why are our virtues used like a club against us?"

I pointed to the black soil that ringed the pyre. "There is man, minus his soul - ashes and grease, a spot on the ground. What equivalent mark does the soul leave behind, if not words and the ideas those words attend? Words like duty and honour, that either describe the longing of a soul to serve some greater purpose, " I pushed at the ashes with the toe of my boot. "or become a set of chains to ensure the subjugation of men."

"And how is it for us, Sr. Almonte?" I asked, suddenly aware of the meaning of my own words. "Do our ideals reflect our hearts, or are they empty of meaning, the devices of men like our President, to demand service, to demand obedience?"

Almonte nodded, a hint of his smile still pinned to his face. I wondered at the effort necessary to keep it there. There was nothing else for us to say. After an uncomfortable silence, I left him behind to contemplate the ashes of the rebel dead.

I am angry. Almonte is not to blame, of course, though I was quick to lash out at him. The death of General Barragan has left me shaken. I am reminded that Santa Anna's hold on our country is tenuous, and I know the maelstrom of atrocities that come from civil wars. Could the corrupt behavior of our Caudillo be any worse than the internal bleeding of another factional power struggle? Would anyone in Mexico City perform in such a superior fashion to Santa Anna, that we would welcome the attending bloodshed?

The answer to my questions is no.

I weep for Mexico.

My course is clear. I will simply do my duty. Santa Anna may still return to Mexico City. Either way, I hope that he will overcome this latest political crisis, and continue in his role. I will do those things that are necessary to aid him.

But my faith in that clear course is shaken. My conversation with Almonte leaves me with questions. Are the seeds of submission planted in a man's virtues? Is virtue in the service of evil still a virtue?

## March 20, 1836. Béjar.

No one is saying anything, but there have been an increasing number of desertions. Santa Anna's answer to such behavior is the death penalty. These men will be caught, and returned to their own battalions, where they will meet a pointless end. I am torn between anger at these fools who shrink from their duty, and anger at the fool who causes them to hold duty in contempt.

I spent this afternoon walking through Béjar. Everywhere, I see signs of the disaster Santa Anna has carved for us - the wounded men lay like wood chips, shaved and scattered through the streets. I see stolen and squandered goods, sold and resold while hundreds of our men shrivel and expire. I see conscripts swallow *aguardiente* and hiss like snakes, until someone uncoils, and lashes out with fist or knife.

Worst of all, I see the future, and the Texas campaign stretches into it without end. The clouds press low today, rolling and smothering the horizon in gray despair. Santa Anna has announced his intention to stay in Texas.

## March 21, 1836. Béjar.

Today, the President's staff gave a tribute to General Barragan, who was in all respects a good and kind man. The ceremony was a simple one, and should have touched Santa Anna's heart, if he had one, since the death of Barragan has caused him discomfort.

Colonel Batres made a speech, mumbling and pausing, as is his way when the audience is large. He stood with his hat under one arm, swaying as he spoke. The sun shone through his hair, silver wisps clinging to his scalp. He looked old, even frail. He lost his place for a moment, and I looked away.

The President used the occasion to display the very worst in his character. He was openly disdainful of the ceremony itself, rolling his eyes, and puffing and exhaling in a way that would have been a sigh, were it not so brief. He called loudly for his medicine box, interrupting the memorial.

The final insult came when he berated Colonel Batres, who has spent a career quietly serving the President, and the Republic. Filisola, the Italian who is our second-in-command, watched without comment.

I spoke up. "Your Excellency," I called, not bothering to moderate my voice, or insert myself between the commander and his staff favorites. "Please control yourself. You do yourself and General

Barragan dishonor by your behavior." There was a sudden, harsh silence. The staff was struck mute by the chance I had taken.

I heard the distant songs of birds through the window.

The President quickly tallied his options. His eyes darted from side to side, and then shut. In an instant, he was the convincing, reasonable man who had once inspired us all. "I apologize to everyone for my impatience," he said, in his most humble voice. "I am scarcely able to control my temper, and the events of this campaign have made things infinitely worse. I beg your indulgence." With this repentance, the President won back the good wishes of the rest of his aides-de-camp, with the possible exception of Batres, who no longer appeared interested in the proceedings.[10]

## March 23, 1836

Béjar. Jubilation at the news of Fannin's surrender at *Encinal del Perdido*;[11] I heard the band play a spirited march, and the *vivas* sounded through the streets. I left my quarters, encountering Batres.

---

[10] Peña mentioned this outburst, but did not mention the personal attack on Colonel Batres.

[11] Encinal del Perdido is the name Mexican sources give to the Battle of Coleto Creek. Fannin attempted to retreat from Goliad to Victoria, but was cut off by General Urrea's force. After a day of fighting, the Texans, without cover or water, were forced to surrender.

"It is over, it is over!" he shouted. He was out of uniform. His shirt was open, and his belly spilled over his trousers. The news caught him half-dressed. "We have won!"

"What is the news?" I asked.

"Urrea defeated Fannin. The war is ended, my friend!" I nodded with slow wonder, relieved that Urrea had succeeded again. The warm morning breeze tossed my hair. I took a deep breath of Texas air. Our Texas.

The moment lasted just seconds. "The war is not over," I said. "Urrea cannot be allowed to finish Houston. Santa Anna will wish to deliver the final blow himself. We will all chase Houston, while Urrea sits on his hands."

"Perhaps you are right," Batres said. "Sr. Urrea will be busy enough. Most of the rebels were captured." There was silence, punctuated by shrill notes from the band that rejoiced in victory. Batres shook his head. "No, you are wrong. There is no longer a need for example," he mumbled. "And the President is an honorable man."

I shrugged. I have no such illusions.

"I see that look in your eyes, Castrillón," Batres said. "You cannot wage war against His Excellency and the Texans at the same time. Remember why we are here, my friend. These pirates, these scoundrels took what was ours, and we have to take it back!" He clutched my arm as he spoke.

"It is more of the same," I snapped.

"They are pirates," he repeated. "Why do you endanger your career, and your future, for the sake of these rebels? There's enough suffering here in the streets of Béjar, enough for a hundred lifetimes!"

I pulled free and dusted my sleeve. "Do you assume that the plight of my own soldiers does not affect me? Do you not see that it is part of the same problem? Santa Anna, who feeds men to battle like slop to a pig, that is the problem!"

Batres stepped back, and began to button his uniform shirt. "I speak only in your best interest," he said, his voice dropping away.

A conscript stepped into the street and fired his weapon into the air, shouting and stumbling away, waving his musket in one hand, and a bottle in another. I let out a slow breath. "It does not matter, Batres, my dear friend," I said, trying to sooth. "His Excellency will not listen to reason. If there are prisoners, then they are already as good as dead. His Excellency will see to it."

Of course, as I spoke, I was thinking of how to approach Santa Anna, and convince him to do otherwise.

## March 25, 1836. Béjar.

Today, I traveled the streets of this place with purpose. I visited each officer in the Toluca, asking what problems they faced, and more to the point, what solutions they offered. It is not enough for a Mexican officer to whine. He must use his mind, and answer the difficulties that have been raised.

Again and again, I heard of hunger, and poor medical provisions. For the latter, I have no answers. Were I a surgeon, I would not sleep until every man had been attended to - this I swear before God.

As for the issue of provisions, I have suggested remedies. The speculators charge two legs and a pair of pants for a meal. This is not a time for men of honor to accumulate money, not when our soldiers suffer the most degrading privations.

I will address this issue with Santa Anna when I speak to him.

## March 26, 1836 Béjar.

Today, I went to see Santa Anna. I waited until dark, as I knew that he would be awake, and because Cós, Ramírez y Sesma, and the other string-puppets would be asleep. I paced the ground in front of the Yturri house, sorting through the words I had chosen. One of the guards must have alerted Santa Anna, for he came to the veranda and welcomed me inside.

"Am I disturbing you, Your Excellency?"

"No, no, of course not, Castrillón. Have a chair, please." He pointed to his table, now covered in maps.

"No thank you, Your Excellency. I have come to discuss an urgent matter." I brushed my hair back from my forehead. "There were prisoners taken at *Encinal del Perdido*."

"Yes, there were. More than three hundred, all told. Fannin was among them. He was trying to take his force from Goliad back to Victoria. Urrea caught them in the open, the fools. The battle lasted only one day." He cocked his head. "You are concerned for their safety?"

I shrugged. "I wish to offer you counsel, my General. That is my duty, and I must meet those obligations. I am certain that you have considered these points, but let me offer them again. Perhaps in a fresh light, they can be appraised fairly."

Santa Anna smiled, raising one eyebrow. "Continue," he said.

"The campaign may be over. The prisoners could be used in bargaining with the Texans."

"I might respond that we do not bargain with pirates," Santa Anna said, pouring himself a glass of wine. The crystal was exquisite. "Wine, Castrillón?"

"No thank you, sir," I said. "Perhaps I used the wrong word. Of course, we would never bargain with pirates if the issue were in doubt, but we have won the war. Our further negotiations must attend to the future of the territory. A prolonged conflict could result in years of hostility "

"What else?"

I stammered. "It may give Houston a reason, or rather, an inducement to surrender. If it is clear that we are amiable to terms, harsh terms to be sure, we could end this campaign "

"It is too late, the orders are delivered. Here. Read them for yourself." He handed me a copy of the communication to Urrea, and turned back to his wine.

The paper on which the order was written was slight, like tissue, and it twitched as I read, dancing in my hands until I realized that my hands were shaking.

Urrea, noble soul, had requested clemency for the prisoners.

"I denied the request, of course," Santa Anna continued. "I have sent Portilla to carry out the order. Urrea cannot be trusted to carry it out alone."

Portilla, my old cell mate![12] It fell to him to deliver the demand for the immediate execution. I do not envy his position.

---

[12] During the early years of the Mexican Revolution, when allegiances changed frequently, Castrillón served time with Portilla in Perote prison for their involvement with Santa Anna's failed coup attempt. Long, Jeff. *Duel of Eagles*. New York: Quill/William Morrow, 1990.

Santa Anna pointed the nearly empty glass of wine at me. "We have had our differences, have we not? No matter. You are a fine officer, and I consider you a candidate for independent command. Still, your antagonism bothers me. If you had not served me so well over the years, if we had not been friends, then I might have disciplined you for your behavior. I want you to consider the necessity for harmony in our staff as the final phase of operations approaches. I will not allow anything to stand in the way of our country's future. Not even an old friendship. To do less would be treason." He crossed over to his desk, and pulled a map from the pile. "Houston must be dealt with. Then we can go home, Castrillón." He held the map up, and tapped his finger on the places he had marked. "Home!" he repeated. "But first, we have unfinished business."

He put the map back on the desk. I opened my mouth to speak, but nothing came to mind.

"You look tired, my friend," he said, his voice calculated to appease. "Get some sleep, will you?"

I excused myself. It was later that I realized I had not discussed the inflated price of provisions. No matter. His Excellency was intractable, and my efforts were pointless.

I walked the streets of Béjar until morning. I did not eat - I don't care to fill any speculator's purse. The wind kept me awake, despite my fatigue. My lower back is troubling me with spasms, and I cannot seem to find a position on my bed that yields comfort. After years of sleeping on the ground, or in a saddle, it is ironic that even a bed cannot relieve the tension. Age is an affront I bear in silence, but there was a time when I would not acknowledge a complaint, even to myself. That time is ending.

## March 30, 1836. Béjar.

I do not know why Santa Anna keeps me in his pocket. He is not stupid, he must know that I despise him. I cannot look him in the eye when he speaks. The sight of him raises bile in the back of my throat.

The deaths of Fannin and his men have further weakened our resolve in this campaign.[13] We are butchers, adding fat to the fire of outrage.

Here in Béjar, the entire attack force numbered 1,800. The death toll for the battle will exceed 600. One man in three gave his life! Can there be a more compelling demonstration of the dedication, and the bravery of the Mexican soldier than this single statistic? Has any general

---

[13] On Sunday, March 27, Colonel Jóse Nicolás Portilla carried out the execution of the prisoners taken in Goliad. More than three hundred men were marched east, ordered to kneel, and were then shot. Very few escaped to tell of the massacre.

been able to call on raw courage as has our President? Have any men, so brave and committed, been used so badly in return?

I can scarcely speak of the suffering. How many of the wounded have died? More than half, and of those who survived thus far, half again will not see the summer. Men with minor wounds, who are not counted when tallying casualty figures, have also died of infection and fever. Men who fought the battle unscathed have suffered as well - disease follows the scene of death, and as I have said a dozen times, we have no physicians to minister to them.

I watch Santa Anna throw his petty tantrums, and insult the staff that has sacrificed so much to serve him. I can scarcely summon common civility. His implied threats against me will not alter my course. I have been imprisoned before.

Tomorrow, we will march to join Ramírez y Sesma. Our forces have been fashioned in a trident, with Ramírez y Sesma's men being the middle prong of an attack that will finish Houston, and finish "Texan Independence." To the south, Urrea takes more than 1,400 men, and across the north, Gaona has 700 more. Somewhere between, Houston has 1000 men. If he will stand and fight, he will be destroyed. The President himself will certainly want to apply the death stroke. There will be one last battle, and Santa Anna's staff will be needed to carry out the victory.

I will serve God and my country, as I always have.  I will busy myself with the logistics of cornering Houston and his rebels.  I will avoid contact with Santa Anna, lest I speak what is in my heart and do some small harm to our army's efforts.  I will seek consolation in my journal entries, and keep my mouth fastened shut.

Then, when the campaign is over, I will be finished with Santa Anna.  I will go home.

# Chapter

# 9

⌣ ✺ ⌣

**March 31, 1836. Béjar.**

God willing, I bid farewell to this awful place forever. We march
again.

Santa Anna said good bye to his "bride" this morning. They spent a
final moment in front of the Yturri house. Tears ran down her chin.
She plucked at his cloak, and each brief contact seemed to require
another touch, as if she wanted to fill her fingers with the memory of his
uniform.

The President was restrained, even aloof. He waved her away,
finally, and the girl was packed off to San Luis Potosí. She paused at the
door of his private coach, discomfited, trying to catch his eye, until the
direction of officers ushered her inside. Santa Anna stood with his back
to the girl, firing orders at his hapless shadow, Caro. Only I was
chastened by the young girl's tears.

And I, in turn, hoped to catch the girl's eye, a fool's errand. I tell
myself that I might have loved this little one, that I would not feast and

then discard her like our President, but is the difference between us merely in degree? Would it matter that I sup, not swallow? Is love no more than acquisition and consumption? One might as well "love" an ear of corn!

I know this, the longing that I felt for the girl is real. It resides inside of me, somewhere near my love of God, and my love of Mexico. I would not desecrate that feeling. I hold it sacred. Does longing become mastication when it wells up and reaches the teeth? If so, it is best that she go south. Absent from the eyes now, absent from the heart later.

All morning, the troops marched past. The faces seem younger to me now, underneath the dust and dirt. They march for Mexico, for Santa Anna. They are trusting young boys, the flower of Mexican youth, petals to be torn away by the whims of the President.

I spent a large portion of the day expediting the exit of our troops from the town. Our officers seem to have forgotten how to facilitate a march. Time tables were ignored.

Our army will leave most of the ordnance behind. Many of the captured pieces are siege mounted, and unfit for travel. We will also leave our flat-bottom boats, and our miners. Our *presidiales* are stationed uselessly to the rear. We will proceed as usual, blind and stupid, trusting in the numerical and qualitative superiority of our force. We risk defeat by our underestimation of this persistent enemy.

## April 2, 1836.  Guadalupe Pass.

Today, the soldiers stopped their march short of the Guadalupe River, in order to pay homage to Santa Anna as he passed.  I watched as the officers took willing part in this farce.  I stood to the rear, and observed.

The President played the Prince, tossing off short waves of the hand as if they were bouquets, to be gathered and treasured by idiots.  Our soldiers, who wear jackets next to their chests, since their shirts have rotted and dropped away, and walk in bare feet, since their sandals have fallen apart, and march with shriveled bellies, taut with the hunger of marching on half rations, all bowed and saluted our illustrious President, and reassured him of their continued fealty.  It was a touching scene.

Almonte followed in the President's steps, forcing his jovial smile. He is an enigma.  He can not defend the President's behavior, yet he attempts to do so with great cheer.  He is not a stupid man.  I am certain that he is quicker-witted than I am.  Why will he not challenge the commander?

The path of our march led us from the sparse deserts before and around Béjar, to the lush lands north.  As if crossing an unseen line, we have stepped into abundance.  The Guadalupe River winds, and twists its way into woodland greenery that undulates with the same breezes that ripple the river. Stones cut the surface of the water, and spill the tumbling waters. The smell of rich, black soil hangs in the wet air. I am not a farmer, but I could be one. I could clear these trees, and plow this soil, fence it off and make it mine.

The land has been generous to the Texans who lived here. Pigs and chickens are plentiful, and corn grows everywhere. Only a Mexican, raised in scarcity, raised in deprivation, could pass through such prosperity, and hoard it, collect it, keep it from consumption, as have our officers. The specter of Mexican troops, guarding carts of corn, while the men continue to starve, serves as testimony to our limitations.

Is this how the *norteamericanos* live? Do they take this plenty for granted?

I entered one of the plantations yesterday, and was startled by what I found. There were cattle everywhere, roaming over the flat farmland. We slaughtered one, and several of the men set about roasting it. I stood by the fire for a while, watching the sizzling fat drip from the beef and pop in the flames, but found that I could not stand waiting. The smell of fresh meat left me weak with hunger.

I wandered into the house, walking through square, sturdy rooms. Two soldiers tore a tapestry from the wall as I passed. A corporal offered me a piece of bitter chocolate that had come from the pantry. I declined, but later gave in to the temptation to pillage when I saw a bookshelf with Greek and Roman works. I took a copy of Aristotle. (It is in English, but I will force my way through it.)

In the corner of one room, I found a child's cradle and cloth doll. A smile was embroidered on the doll's face. I gave thought to taking the cradle with me, and giving it to the first child I encountered, but the impulse was silly. I had no intention of spending the day with a cradle under my arm. I clutched my book and left the house. Later, I saw a soldier with the same cradle, playing a jest with the doll.

Soldiers stumbled across the grounds, drunk on wine from the house cellar. Some of the men danced, draped in quilts, to entertain the *soldaderas*. Others sang and made noises as if they were instruments. I did not begrudge the men their comedy. If a man who has gone without water comes upon a lake, what does he do? Sip from the banks? No, he jumps in! It is to be expected.

The occupants of the plantation fled before we arrived, leaving everything behind. Ramírez y Sesma had passed by a slightly different route, otherwise, the contents of the plantation would have been added to the "Customs House."[1]

---

[1] This was the name given to Ramírez y Sesma's quarters, where large amounts of booty were stored and sold.

In the field, we found a well, more than a hundred feet deep, lined with brick. The water was cool and sweet. We found hams in the smokehouse, I took one. (The meat was too rich, and upset my stomach. By contrast, the roasted beef was delicious.) The barn had various pieces of machinery, and even a bucket of nails!

When the rain ended, late in the evening, I walked through the woods alone. The humid air was sweet and thick with pollen. I felt reborn, as if spring could take the ache from my joints. A dozen different wild flowers laced the edges of my path, brushing the grass with purples, reds, blues, and yellows. Birds unseen sang and chattered, and one whooped in celebration. The cacophony of chirps and whistles was a delight. My boots sank into the dark soil at each step. Squirrels pitched themselves about at my approach, and I laughed at their mischief.

The sound of my own laughter startled me. I have been extraordinarily somber throughout the course of this campaign, and that is against my nature. Here, with my boot heels sinking into the soft earth, I find my voice. I shout at the trees, and watch the birds scatter into the indigo sky. This too, is my Mexico. For just a moment, I am at peace here.

## April 3, 1836.  Guadalupe Pass.

When we march today, we will leave Filisola and his command behind.  Santa Anna is anxious to catch Ramírez y Sesma, and in his haste, he neglects the establishment of outposts, or communication points.  As it was before, and as it will be again. I have grown weary of repeating myself.

I am taking an active role in scouting, as the prospect of wandering blind through the Texas landscape does not appeal to me.

## April 8, 1836.  San Felipe.

We arrived yesterday, and discovered a town put to the torch.  Two hundred people once lived here.  Now it is a stubble of burnt wood and cinders.  Houston has demonstrated his ruthless resolve in this matter, San Felipe was the original Anglo settlement in Texas, and as such, had a special place in the heart of the rebels.

On the opposite side of the Brazos, marksmen in trenches take from us a soldier here, and a soldier there.  We have been shelling these rebels, and peppering them with musket fire for two days.  It is maddening, they are clearly a rear guard engaged in a delaying tactic that succeeds more from our lack of preparedness than from their cleverness.  If we had swimmers, or riflemen of our own, we would chase these rebels from their position in hours, not days.

I was late to the staff meeting today, after correcting several officers who still refuse to attend to the remaining oxen. If these idiots were forced to wear the harness and drag supplies behind them, would they then realize the value of our animals?

I expected to be castigated for my tardiness. I was ignored. Santa Anna poked his fingers at still another map, while his officers listened to the attending tirade. "Our scouts tell me there are no rebels between the Colorado and the Trinity river. The pirates have left their homes. They run to survive. Houston is a coward."

Almonte cleared his throat. "The campaign will not be over," he said, "until Houston is destroyed. In this running game, he has us at a disadvantage. He knows this country, and his force is mobile. We move at a pace with snails."

"True" Santa Anna agreed. "And for that very reason, I have been considering an idea. We may yet end this war while Houston plays hide-and-seek." He backed away from the table full of maps, and produced a medicine box. After a pause, he pointed at Harrisburg. "This is where the rebel government has sequestered itself. Here, these criminals plot their misadventures. If I were to strike Harrisburg, and catch them unprepared, then the campaign would be over, would it not?" He glanced at Ramírez y Sesma, who stood off to the side of the tent, sulking.

"Can this be done?" Almonte asked.

Santa Anna smiled, and pounded the table. "It will be done, gentlemen! I believe this campaign will be over in a week!"

Almonte gave a broad smile. "That would be a bold stroke, Your Excellency. It would end the war, and save Mexican lives."

As the meeting adjourned, Santa Anna caught my glance for a moment, and then turned his back on me, grabbing Almonte by the elbow and leading him off into another discussion.

Ramírez y Sesma pointed at the two of them, and whispered, "That is how you behave, if you intend to secure an independent command, Castrillón."

Indeed. As if I were a donkey, contemplating a carrot. As if I would serve our Commander one single second past what duty and chivalry demand.

## April 11, 1836. San Felipe.

We have been unable to cross to the east bank of the Brazos. I am reminded of Béjar, and I am afraid that we will be stuck here, firing at men in trenches for days to come. I have been up and down the river, looking for an alternative route. There is a ferry, but it is in rebel hands, and it would be a simple thing for them to sever the guideline at our approach.

## April 12, 1836.  Fort Bend.

Today we saw an amazing end to the impasse at the Brazos.  We went to the west bank at Thompson's Ferry, and there found a Negro slave operating the boat.  The President and staff arrived in advance of the troops, and managed not to give away our position.

We stood at a distance, watching the Negro.  He appeared to be alone.  "I have an idea," Almonte said, stripping his jacket.  "I believe I can fool this man.  I am going to convince him to bring the ferry across."  He set the jacket on a bush, and tugged his collar loose.  "If it appears that the ruse has failed, shoot him.  Don't let him cut the guideline."

"If we go ahead and shoot him now, we can cross over on the guideline itself," I said.  "There is no reason to risk yourself."

"We want the ferry, not just a share of the rope," Almonte said.  He put a hand on my shoulder.  "Don't worry, my English is good."

Santa Anna nodded, and positioned a few men near the bank, in case supporting fire was needed.  Almonte gave us his smile, and headed into the clearing.

He called for the Negro to bring the ferry over to the west bank. "I am a Texan," he shouted, waving from the river's edge. "I need to join my unit. [Sam] Houston needs every man he can [get]."[2]

The Negro stared at him for a full ten seconds before moving. I held my breath, hand on my pistol, certain that the Negro was not fooled. He was more than sixty yards out, and I could imagine our volley missing, while the thin dark man with the pole slid the ferry out of range. Or perhaps he would saw at the guideline with a knife, cutting himself free, sending the ferry down-river.

At last, he planted the pole, and began moving the ferry to our side of the river bank. I took a breath. Almonte waited in silence as the boat approached, a slight breeze tossing his hair.

Then, just as astonishing, the President himself leapt from the bushes and pushed the slave, who was thin as a bundle of sticks, to the deck of the ferry. The slave lay there, bare feet pumping in the air, covering his face. We took possession of the boat, and made immediate arrangements to begin transporting our men to the opposite bank. The enemy will have no choice but to fall back.

I must admit a certain admiration for the way Almonte handled the situation. The slave might have been armed, and the deception itself

---

[2] Castrillón wrote Almonte's words in English: "'Sayam' Houston needs all the men he can 'gayat'." He may have been poking fun at the Texas accent.

required cool nerves. When I congratulated him, he seemed genuinely pleased at my comment. Later he added, "The President was courageous as well." I did not agree. By the time Santa Anna left his hiding place, it was clear that the slave was harmless. Wrestling a stack of bones does not take courage.

## April 14, 1836. Thompson's Ferry.

Our troops have massed on the east bank of the Brazos, and the rebels that stalled our approach have abandoned their position. The President will carry out his plan against Harrisburg personally. I wish him success.

## April 15, 1836. Harrisburg.

This morning, at 2 A.M., Santa Anna entered Harrisburg with a company of dragoons. The town was nearly deserted. The so-called government of the Texans had evacuated just hours earlier. The only Texans left in town were three luckless printers, trying to close out one last edition of the Telegraph and Texas Register, a batch of lies that pretends to be a newspaper. I have no patience for newspapers, and I was amused to hear that the President threw the press into Buffalo Bayou.

Almonte questioned the prisoners, and learned that the government had moved thirty leagues away, to New Washington. I am told that

Santa Anna's frustration bubbled over into a rage - he stood for a moment, fists clenched and shaking as if to squeeze the life from his palms, a single throbbing vein popping from his forehead. Then he let loose a string of curses, profane execrations that ended in a shriek. The officer who related the events managed an uncanny imitation of Santa Anna's manner, and I believe his account. I have seen similar outbursts.

Then our President put Harrisburg to the torch.

As evening fell, I watched the scattered flames dance over the town. More burns there than Texan buildings. Another chance to end this campaign crouches in the embers, reduced to ash. How many chances will our President squander? When will his chances run out?

As Napoleon advanced into Russia, it was the Russians who put Russian land to the torch, so that the French would derive no comfort. We are burning Mexico. Does our Napoleon have it backwards?

## April 17, 1836. Galveston Bay.

Today I accompanied Almonte on another cavalry patrol. With the absence of *presidiales*, I have made myself available for scouting missions. (What else can I do? I am a man of action, trapped in a situation where action is futile. I am an aide-de-camp, with no one to advise or assist.) We pushed closer to New Washington, hoping to catch the so-called government before they evacuated. On the way, I had occasion to question Almonte about our President's tantrum of the previous day.

Almonte smiled his usual smile, and offered the usual excuses for the President's excesses. His Excellency is tired. His Excellency is under great pressure due to military concerns in Texas, and political concerns in Mexico City. His Excellency has never fully recovered from his illness of last January. Almonte is a skilled apologist, and I would gladly have filled the cup of forgiveness to overflowing, had I not known what both of us know - Santa Anna is a petty tyrant that is out of control, and inadequate to the task of command.

We skirted the bay, winding through the trees, silent. The dragoons were quiet, but inattentive. Scouting was a burden to them. I kept my eyes on the ground, looking for signs. I must confess that I do not have a tracker's sense, but it seemed that I ought not doze in the saddle. Almonte kept his eyes in front, and to the sides, looking for Texans.

From time to time, I would glance at Almonte, wondering at the man. I was unaware that I was about to revise my opinion of him.

We came out of a grove of trees, stopping at the very shore line, and found ourselves just yards away from a rowboat that carried off several men and a woman. Out in the bay, we could see a Texas navy ship waiting. A look of surprise and panic struck the men in the boat. The woman gave us a forlorn glance, and turned away, huddling with her back to us. The rebels bent to their oars, crouching, as if they could hide. Some of our dragoons leveled their muskets. The targets were too close to miss. Then Almonte spoke.

"Hold your fire!" The amicable smile was gone, and the sheer force of his personality demanded that his orders be followed. "There is a woman in the boat. You will not fire."

One cavalry officer stared at Almonte. "Sir, those men are part of the rebel government."

Almonte turned to him, and said in a low voice that sounded like iron, "I am not in the business of waging war on women or children." The officer nodded, hanging his head. The rowboat moved out into the bay.[3]

Riding away, we were contemplative. Some of the dragoons were angry, muttering, and slapping their mounts, regretting another squandered opportunity. Almonte was quiet, and seemed to be absorbed by his thoughts. I made it a point to ride next to him, and when he glanced my way, I nodded. He offered a smile that was modest, yet more endearing than the broad, jovial grin that usually graces his countenance. We spoke only to each other the rest of the way back, ignoring the sullen dilettantes that traveled with us.

---

[3] One of the men in the rowboat was David G. Burnet, the interim president of the newly formed Texas Republic. The woman mentioned was his wife.

There are lines over which this man will not cross. I respect Almonte. We both hold certain principles sacred, and defend those principles when we can, despite our commander, who operates under different precepts. We both put duty before personal considerations, and we both love Mexico.

He is a Cavalier. I did him an injustice by my low estimation of his behavior at the counsel of war before the battle for *el Alamo* I recognized his integrity, but I did not understand why he failed to echo my position. Since my tactics have not succeeded, it is clear that my anger was once again misplaced.

Almonte is better at hiding his frustration, and for this, he deserves praise, not censure. We chose our paths carefully, trying both to serve Santa Anna, and to guide him. I do not believe that I have the President's ear, and I think Almonte still does. I have been more aggressive than Almonte in confronting our President, but I have also been less sensible in the battles I choose. I peck away, like a bird at seed, and nothing is solved. I am the one who has failed, not Almonte.

I took Santa Anna to task for killing prisoners as pirates, not soldiers, and for his behavior at General Barragan's memorial ceremony. What sort of causes are these, when our men suffer? Yet, in my defense, how does one approach a commander who exhibits so little compassion for his own men that he steals from them, starves them, and robs meaning from their deaths?

I wish Almonte luck. I no longer wish to serve our commander. I cannot stand the sight of him.

## April 18, 1836. On the Brazos River.

Today, a Texas ship called the *Yellow Stone* steamed past our men at several points along the river. The rebels had piled cotton bales on the deck to protect the men that manned her. Our musket fire had no effect.

Drawn by the sound of gunfire, I witnessed the encounter from a distance. Our men had decided to attack, and tried to lasso the ship's smokestacks. There was no apparent plan, and our soldiers behaved like amateurs.

The cavalry pounded along the river, shouting and tossing rope. The *Yellow Stone* shot smoke and sparks that billowed out into grey clouds hanging on the water. The ship's paddle slapped a wake of foam onto the grassy banks. Our soldiers cursed and dodged rifle balls, reeling empty lassos back from the river.

I could not bear to watch, and rode back to join the staff a half league to the rear. Later, I was relieved to hear that none of our soldiers were hurt in the debacle.

This evening, I sat down to a meal of smoked ham and fruit, washed down with brandy. My appetite has been neglected, and the repast was delightful, but the memory of the attack on the steamboat soured my stomach, and I ate very little. I will not stuff myself with rebel goods.

I imagine that the Texans had a great laugh at our expense as we tried to rope the great machine of the *norteamericanos* - foolish, pastoral Mexicans! Our march into Texas has been cause for their amusement. I long for battle. I want to exact a soldier's price for that amusement.

## April 19, 1836

I rode out in advance of the main body of troops, again, this time in the company of Colonel Trevino. The terrain was uneven, choked with pines, gums, oaks, and a dozen other trees I could not name. The forest floor was covered in layers of ferns and mosses. The air was a hot, fusty blanket. Sweat rolled down Trevino's ample face, shining on his cheeks and forehead, and pooling in his collar. The morning sun chased swarms of insects into the air, and they seemed to like the smell of Trevino, because they followed his head like a tiny cloud. He waved them off, and mopped the sweat with his sleeve, and then waved some more, always moving, and so he continued to sweat.

Shortly after noon, we captured one of the *norteamericanos* who was stationed as an advanced scout. His horse was tied off at edge of a clearing, and when he saw us, he froze, and then bolted into a thicket. I was forced to dismount, and follow him in. Branches whipped my face, cutting my cheek, and tearing at my jacket. When the rebel scout paused to check my pursuit, I caught him from behind, and knocked him to the ground, dislodging his knife, and pinning him flat.

Colonel Trevino, who had followed me, fell wheezing on top of the man, and grabbed his arms. Later, Trevino told me, "You are fit for an old man." I told him that old men sit on porch swings and eat soup. I am a soldier.

We questioned the rebel, and discovered that Houston's army was stationed on the left side of Groce's Plantation, and that his force is down to less than 800 men, due to desertions. It is the scout's opinion that Houston must soon fight, lest his entire force defect.

I reported this information to Santa Anna, who has been resting at the Morgan plantation. He greeted the news with no particular excitement. I expressed my hope that the intelligence served some purpose, and left without further comment.

Encountering the rebel scout was fortuitous. I have persisted in my efforts to reconnoiter the area, more out of stubbornness than hope. If Santa Anna does not act quickly, however, he will render this bit of information useless, and rob my last hope for significant action.

# Chapter

# 10

**April 20, 1836.  San Jacinto.**

We put New Washington to the torch today, and then moved north, to Lynch's Ferry, in order to trap Houston and his army.  It was with much surprise that we discovered Houston's men waiting for us, battle lines drawn.  We spoiled for a confrontation, and they did not have the sense to disappoint us.

It was unclear how much of Houston's force we had encountered.  At the other end of the meadow, two small rebel cannon were visible, attended by a handful of men.  Dragging our cannon *"El Volcan"* through the mud over the past few days has been maddeningly difficult.  I heard Santa Anna complain to Captain Urriza, "How did they manage to move two cannon through this terrain?"

There were no visible signs of the rebel infantry, they were well hidden in the oak trees draped with Spanish moss, but it was clear from the noise that a sizable body of pirates waited for us across the meadow.

We moved *"El Volcan"* into a copse of trees in the center of the meadow. Santa Anna personally directed the fire of the piece from the cover of the huge red and white oaks, his staff in attendance. One round we fired seemed to strike home - severed tree limbs plunged down around one of the enemy's cannon, and the rebel gun crew fell back with shouts and curses. Santa Anna exchanged smiles of congratulation with Captain Urriza, while the rest of the staff burst into cheers.

I stayed behind, directing our infantry to defensive positions. I assumed that our Commander would order an attack, particularly if the rebel guns were silenced. He had ordered the infantry and cavalry columns into line, with no further attention to position, the whole of his efforts being taken by the two rebel cannon. It seemed prudent to set up a defensive perimeter.

The rebel gun was not disabled. As I approached to report our readiness to defend the grove, a shot came crashing through the trees. The thunderclap of splintering wood sent our men tumbling back into the grove. Captain Urriza stood wounded, blood running down his left arm, his uniform sleeve shredded. He stepped forward, tripping against the carriage wheel of our cannon. Santa Anna, who had been observing the enemy position by telescope, was anxious to assess the damage.

"Did we lose the cannon?" he demanded. Colonel Delgado assured him that *El Volcan* was still operable. Captain Urriza sat, back to the firing tube, staring at his arm.

Santa Anna pointed across the meadow. "You must return fire," he said.

A sergeant from the gun crew approached to report the damage. "The shot destroyed an ammunition crate, and killed two mules as well."

The pack animals suffer the worst of it again, I thought.

Colonel Delgado began peeling back Sr. Urriza's sleeve to discover the severity of the wound. Bits of wood were imbedded in the flesh. A shard of metal had torn through the bicep without hitting bone. With luck, the Captain would not lose the arm.

"I am wounded, General," the Captain moaned.

Santa Anna gave Captain Urizza a glance, and then turned back to Colonel Delgado. "Have your men fire a round of grape," he demanded.

I left Colonel Delgado to Santa Anna's directions, and escorted Captain Urriza to the rear.

"You will be fine," I told him. "The bone is intact. You will have a scar to show your grandchildren. Have you any linens left? Your wound needs to be dressed."

"I donated them all in Béjar."

I nodded. "I'm sure we can come up with a clean shirt. Perhaps I will raid His Excellency's tent."

Captain Urizza stopped and grabbed me with his good arm. "He looked right through me! Am I a window?"

"Six pounds of roundshot fired at your chest - you might well have been!" I joked.

In the following hours, we exchanged fire, the rebel cannon doing the greater part of the damage. When a round struck *El Vocan*, damaging the carriage, we were forced to withdraw, lest we lose the piece.

Rebel cavalry tried to capture the cannon as we worked to remove it. It was a stupid blunder on their part, and they paid in blood for their recklessness. The sight of these renegades, brandishing a flag with a half-naked woman, infuriated our men.

I had returned to the copse of trees, and was there to greet the charge. I thought, the weeks of waiting are over. Finally! We are soldiers, and now we will do what soldiers do. The sentiment was echoed by the men in different ways, from the firmly set jaw, to the clenched fist, to the whispered invitation, "Come on, come on!"

The rebels pounded across the meadow, horses thundering on the tall grass. A single volley from the *norteamericanos* filled the air with smoke, and threw our men into momentary confusion, but did no real damage. Our cavalrymen returned the charge with lowered lances, surrounding many rebels who had dismounted to fire and reload. We dispatched the lot of them with lances and musket fire. They returned to the safety of the thicket, moving with the sluggish confusion of a cattle herd. I shouted my excitement and triumph along with the men. The staff was of a mind to attack the rebels then, but Santa Anna had "plans" of his own.

These plans included a retreat from the open field. I do not begrudge the decision to take a defensive stance - I myself had been concerned with defensive positioning before the exchange of fire. The force in front of us was equal in strength to ours, perhaps greater, and the bulk of their men were hidden in the woods. An argument could be made against any attack without the full advantage of numbers. Santa Anna sent word to Cós to hasten reinforcements, certainly a prudent move. In the event of a night attack, we could make good use of a fortified position, that is to say, the tactics our Commander chose could be justified.

I would not have been so cautious. When I think of the way the rebel horsemen stumbled about the open field, I believe I would have taken advantage then, and thrown those confused pirates into the swamps. A quick thrust, directly on the heels of their retreat, might have led to the capture of their cannon. Perhaps I am too bold, too impatient.

Having decided against an aggressive posture, Santa Anna withdrew to the edge of the lake, the very lowest point on the plain, with forest, swamp, and water blocking a retreat, should we be thrown back. In this, the most idiotic place possible, we set up our line of defense.

We spent the night preparing for an attack at dawn. The men were tired from the march, and the day's hostilities, but there was to be no rest for any of us. Santa Anna was seen at all points, berating the men, running from here to there, wringing his hands, and personally directing each detail of the construction of the barricades that offer no real hope of cover from fire. The five-foot high barrier was made of pack saddles, dirt, and sacks of beans and hard bread.

I helped facilitate the construction of the barrier. I followed my orders. As we neared completion, I was struck fresh with the absurdity of our efforts. We had waited so long to find Houston, only to hide from him. It occurred to me that we would not defeat the rebels, that Santa Anna would not meet the measure of necessity.

As I walked the length of the barricade, I came upon an officer directing some of the construction. If he recognized me, he offered no sign of doing so. I believe he was the same lieutenant who built the Rio Frio bridge without tools on the march north. He looked thinner (but then all of us look thinner!), and his uniform was worn, though clean. He offered a weary salute. I asked him what he thought of the barricade.

He stared at me, and I could not tell if he had suddenly placed me, or if he was calculating the consequences of an honest answer. He tapped a sack of hard bread at the top of the pile. "When I eat this bread, I think, this is surely the hardest substance known. Now I think it should be harder still, since it will be required to stop a fifty-caliber ball."

I nodded. I had conflicting urges. I wanted to explain, to separate myself from the blame that surely must be fixed for this atrocity against common sense. Instead I was silent. I have served Santa Anna, and without my complicity, the lieutenant would not be stacking bread like a baker. I have earned his scorn.

"Carry on, Lieutenant," I whispered. The good man turned back to his labors.

As I passed the center of the barricade, Santa Anna came bustling by, with Caro in tow. It was then that I had another confrontation with our President.

"Higher, higher," he muttered. He stopped, staring past me at the stacks of dry goods, a warehouse turned out for battle. "Higher," he muttered again. I was not certain if he was addressing me, so I asked him to repeat himself. He flew into a rage.

"I have grown weary of you questioning!" he bellowed.

I was taken aback. "Your Excellency, I am merely asking you to repeat yourself."

"I know what you are doing," he said, stepping closer. His voice dropped to a whisper, in order to deprive the men who had stopped everything to watch the President's tirade. Caro stood staring, as usual.

"I know what you are doing," he repeated. "You question my every decision, and test the very limits of our association. All right, Castrillón. You do not approve of our strategy. Why? Go on, speak up."

"Very well," I said, hot blood rushing to my face. "I do not think sacks of hard bread make an acceptable barricade."

He stared at me without speaking, his arms locked behind his back. It was dark, and I could not see his eyes at all. He took a deep breath, and then stepped back. "Caro! See to it that the men gather branches from the woods to strengthen the barricade." Caro frowned and scurried away.

"There," he said. "Is that satisfactory?"

I swallowed a laugh, badly, and had to turn away.

"Castrillón," he whispered. "Do you realize that you put your future at risk?" His voice was choked with fury, and I was ashamed for him. I struggled to regain my composure, glad of the darkness that hid my expression. "I don't know what to say, my President."

"Be candid, damn you!" he blustered. "I will know what is in your mind!"

I took one huge breath, and let it out slowly. So it had come to this. Just as well.

"I do not wish to serve you any longer than duty requires," I said, careful to soften my voice, and the blow.

"You wish to retire?"

"I wish to retire from any army commanded by you."

For a minute, perhaps two, we faced each other. The chirp and whistle of swamp birds, and the low hum of insects were like music, and the men worked in rhythm, hauling and stacking. I endured the silence without comment.

At length, Santa Anna turned, as if suddenly disinterested, calling after Caro. I stood, arms behind my back, watching as they scuttled away. The bully would need to vent his frustration, and in that brief moment, I felt pity for Caro.

As I write, men are carrying bundles of sticks to the barricade. The mind reels.

(*Translator's Note*: This ends the last full entry in Castrillón's journal. A final entry, written the day of the Battle of San Jacinto, has been included at the end of the manuscript, as an epilogue.)

# Letter

(Translator's Note: The following letter, written by Samuel Kaufman to his wife, offers an eyewitness account of General Castrillón's death.)

## April 23, 1836

My Dear One,

The running is over. Sam Houston and the Army of Texas have whipped Santana! I have had not a moment to spare until now, and I am stealing a few moments to write to you. No, the food is not good. Today we ate fried squirrel, but there was no buttermilk to do it up right. I told the boys how you bake small birds inside a sweet potato, and they were properly envious.

The battle itself was ferocious and terrible. I thank almighty God that you are a woman, and spared such grim responsibilities. We did what we needed to do, though it is clear to me that some did much more than what ought to have been done.

Sam Houston had been in full retreat for weeks. We were near the San Jacinto River, and Sam asked if we were of a mind to fight. I was tired of pulling foot anyway.

The 21st, just two short days ago, we crossed the plains of San Jacinto in the afternoon, while the Mexicans slept. Earlier in the day, they had taken reinforcements, but that was to our liking. Why bite the same pig twice?

We ate, and then after 3 P.M., we assembled in the grove of oaks that fringed Buffalo Bayou. We stood in two thin lines, a thousand yards wide, ready for action. I carried a rifle, a pistol, and a Bowie knife.[1] Sam Houston himself led the army forward. I'll allow I was a little streaked. I did not want to take some Mexican's musket ball.

As we marched, the band played "Come to the Bower. I will not repeat the words to you, as they are of a questionable nature.[2] We came on, silent save the music. The Mexicans slept while we crossed the field, to their eternal regret.

---

[1] The weapon was already famous, and in widespread use.

[2] Will you come to the bow'r I have shaded for you?
Our bed shall be roses all spangled with dew.
There under the bow'r on roses you'll lie
with a blush on your cheek but a smile in your eye!

Our two cannon, the Twin Sisters, let fly, waking the enemy, but causing great devastation on their ranks. We rolled the cannon to within seventy yards of the Mexican line as it formed, and fired again. Then our infantry swept in, myself present as well.

There was a moment, me thrashing through the tall grass, weapons in hand, that I felt the swelling in the chest, like some great deed was being done. I look back at that moment now, and shake my head.

What I saw will stick with me forever. I would not mention it to you, but we have always been nothing but honest with each other, and it's a thing you need to know in order to understand my feelings in this matter. The Mexicans tried to throw up a line of defense. They managed some cannon fire, and a ragged volley that hit little or nothing. Our return fire dropped the Mexican general from his horse.

The Mexicans ran, and left the general alone to face us. He was an older man, with silver streaked black hair that hung past his neck. He was taller than the other Mexicans, as tall or taller than I am, and he was wounded in the leg. He hauled himself up on an ammunition box, and shouted at us in Spanish, which as you know, I have been well schooled in. He said, "I have been in forty battles and never showed my back! I am too old to do it now!" He crossed his arms, and folded them over his chest, and there he stood.

I thought, this man has sand! though it did not help him any. General Rusk shouted for the men not to shoot, and he pushed aside some of their guns, but battle fever was on us. Some of the men passed Rusk and fired away, and riddled the old general full of musket balls.

That is where my tale of battle ends. I stood there for a while, staring at the Mexican General's body, watching it twitch on the grass. Then I helped to secure the captured cannon while the others moved on.

The fighting was over soon enough. It didn't last but twenty minutes. I'd had my fill of it anyway. It wasn't a battle really, more of a hunt. I am told that some of the Mexicans got hung up in a swamp near here, and our men made a turkey-shoot of them.

The next day, I walked the plain, through the waist-high grass. There were dead Mexicans everywhere. Flies were thick, and the smell was awful.[3]

Don't think less of me, but it seems that wars are made up of one-sided battles. Good men and heroes are slaughtered, and many are forgotten. Old Sam Houston is already being called the *Hero of San*

---

[3] The bodies, including Castrillón's, were never buried. Houston ordered that the Mexican dead at San Jacinto lay untouched, carrion for the wolves and coyotes, despite the protests of the widow who owned the land. In time, the bodies turned to bare bones, which cattle chewed for the salt.

*Jacinto*, and rightfully so, but what about that old Mexican, cold as a wagon tire, and laying to rot in the battlefield?

I will write more later. Right now, we are waiting for the Mexican army to try to turn the worm. Don't worry yourself, though. They brought in Santana himself, captured yesterday, which ought to end the whole thing outright, unless somebody decides to kill the slippery devil. I will qualify for a huge land grant, should our advantage be maintained.

Take care of the children. Tell Ryan[4] that his Daddy said to behave himself. I love you all—

Samuel Kaufman

---

[4] Samuel Kaufman's son, aged six at the time of the battle.

# Epilogue

(<u>Translator's Note</u>: This last fragment was written by General Castrillón just before the Battle of San Jacinto.)

## April 21, 1836. San Jacinto.

We spent the morning waiting for Houston to attack. Nothing happened. Then, at 9 A.M., Cós arrived with reinforcements. The rebels must have been sorely disheartened to see another 500 men arrive. They will not attack us today - we are too strong in number. Though I have not slept, I am not particularly tired, but instead, anxious for the end of the rebellion. Our President, however, has finally decided that he was fatigued, and retired to his red and white tent.[1]

---

[1] Castrillón does not mention the legendary Emily Morgan, and there is good evidence to suggest that the legend of the "Yellow Rose of Texas" is false. There was an Emily D. West, a free woman of color in her later thirties, who was captured along with others when Santa Anna took Morgan's plantation, and forced to march to Buffalo Bayou several days later. Though a possible rape victim, there is no documentation showing that she was in Santa Anna's tent the day of the battle.

Colonel Delgado approached me to complain about the fortifications, on which we expended so much effort. Our troops are left with no room to maneuver, and with natural barriers to our rear, we have no place for a retreat. The ground is level - our defensive position offers us no advantage. The rebels sit in the woods, waiting with long rifles.

Though we stood within easy hearing of Santa Anna's tent, I could not soften my answer, and found that my voice assumed an impassioned life of its own. I told him, "What would you have me do, my friend? I am aware of everything you have told me, but I am powerless to change a single aspect. The man is too busy adding to his own legend. He has no time for ordinary sense!"

Colonel Delgado sighed and left. I know that I have somehow failed him, but I do not know what more I can do. Our President has been chasing Houston for weeks, and has split his army into pieces in order to catch him, something that could have been accomplished with more favorable odds had we brought the *presidiales*, who know this country. As it is, we are scarcely larger in number than Houston, and the moment for bold action has passed.

The other officers do not share my pessimism. The mood of the camp is jubilant. Houston is here, and we will have him, whether he attacks or not, or so it seems. This campaign was Santa Anna's, either to win or to lose. I do not quite share the staff's faith in our sure victory.

A short time ago, Sr. Batres[2] came to me, champagne in hand, wishing to celebrate great victory. He pulled a mongrel dog behind him, leashed with a length of rope. "Here is my new friend," he said. The dog was a matted yellow thing that seemed little more than ribs and fur. "I found him wandering around in the marsh, looking for Texans," he said. He knelt, and addressed the dog. "They're over in the trees. Can you smell them?"

Batres was drunk, and I did not wish to berate him. He leaned close when he spoke, and he smelled of alcohol and bad skin.

"Here, my friend," I said, offering him a platter that I had barely touched. "I formed a mess of my own, and took back my cook from Santa Anna. You should eat something."

He took the platter and sat down on a rock, landing heavily. He offered a bite of the food to the mongrel, who lunged at the food. "No,

---

2 Colonel Batres died in the Battle of San Jacinto. He tried to escape the battlefield by way of Peggy Lake, the scene of some of the worst killing. Nicholas Labadie, a French-Canadian surgeon who served the Texans during the campaign, found Batres mired in mud up to his knees. Labadie offered a hand to the helpless officer just seconds before a Texan shot Batres point-blank in the forehead, splattering Labadie with blood in the process. (Hardin,Stephen. Texian Illiad: A Military History of the Texas Revolution. Austin: University of Texas Press, 1994.)

no, not all of it!" he scolded, trying to take back a portion, but the dog snapped at his fingers, and he slapped it away, leaving the platter empty. "Stupid dog," he declared. "It does not realize how lucky it is." Batres stared to slip from his seat on the rock. He righted himself, and called after the dog. "Would you bite the generous hand, you stupid mongrel?" The dog sat at the end of the rope, wolfing down the last of the food.

Then Batres smiled, waving his bottle. He produced two glasses. "The war is over, over. Soon, His Excellency will order an attack, and we will crush these infidels." He shoved the bottle at me. I took a glass, if only to appease my friend. When his attention wandered, I let the liquid trickle into the dry, stiff grass.

"Do you not believe this is over?" he asked. I shrugged. He tugged gently on the mongrel's leash. "Do you not see how hopeless Houston is? We have thousands of men in the field. He has hundreds. We will crush him." He paused to drain his glass.

"Santa Anna may still find a method to defame us all." I said.

"Do you not love your country?" Batres demanded.

"Of course I do." I said.

"Santa Anna is Mexico." he declared.

I shrugged. "It is generally believed so, though when Santa Anna dies, Mexico will not. But let us not argue."

Batres nodded, and sighed. His eyes were red and teary. "I hate this place, this Texas. The mosquitoes eat me alive. Damn this place."

Poor Batres! The campaign has left him old. I see it in his eyes. He no longer believes in anything, and it has drained his marrow. The hardships, from poor rations to miserable weather, the folly and the failures, and the pointless deaths of brave comrades are not enough to defeat a Mexican soldier, certainly not a professional like Batres. But to lose one's beliefs! That is too much to bear.

I have come to question everything as well. I have lived by an honorable code, and I have seen that code exposed as selfish buffoonery, honor only visible by its absence. I have tried to be a virtuous man, to serve Santa Anna and my country, to do my duty. Yet I have had occasion to doubt our Commander, to question my duty, even to curse love.

Now I sit here in this swamp looking at the hyacinths and the gray moss that decorates the trees, and I think how lovely it is here. I am cheered by the smell of tall grass and wildflowers, and by the warm hand of the sun on my neck. I love this land because it is part of Mexico. My Mexico.

It is as if my beliefs are suddenly unfettered, set free from the incompetent little despot who has directed my service these many years. And unfettered, these beliefs emerge from the dark box of doubt where I have kept them, nearly hidden, and I find them to be potent medicine for what has ailed my soul.

Honor does not depend on Antonio López de Santa Anna. It depends on my heart, and the hearts of my countrymen. Mexico's finest hours lie ahead. Our story will not end here.

And if what I believe is a lie, so be it - it is a lie I have chosen. A man should choose beautiful lies.

My thoughts are half-formed - no matter. I have time to trace them to the truth. I have a new purpose for my writing -

Cannon fire. It begins.

# Afterword

Though General Castrillón was a real man, *The Breach* is a work of fiction. I mention this, because the author-as-editor device contains an element of subterfuge. I chose the form because it lent a certain tone of authority to the novel, and because it allowed me to park some expository material into footnotes, out of the way of a casual reading.

The four professors mentioned in the preface are real, deserving of real thanks. I would also thank Kathryn Lang of SMU Press for her advice. Allen Wier, and C.D. Huneycutt were kind enough to provide cover blurbs for the first edition.

A special thanks to my sister, Karin Kaufman, who helped edit my mistakes. And without the support of my parents, Harold and Elinor Kaufman, the book would never have been written.

Charles Kaine of Last Knight Publishing Company was courageous enough to take a chance on the book, just about the time I was ready to bury it in Emily Dickinson's dresser. For that, I will be forever grateful.

Finally, a huge thank-you to Stephen L. Hardin, who spent a great deal of time catching the historical mistakes in the manuscript. I think I did a fair job of piecing together my General's story, but I couldn't have done it without his help.